ELEANOR FARJEON'S POEMS FOR CHILDREN

# ELEANOR FARJEON'S
# POEMS
# FOR CHILDREN

J. B. Lippincott Company
Philadelphia and New York

LIBRARY OF CONGRESS CATALOG CARD NUMBER 51–11164

*This book contains the complete text of four volumes of verse by Eleanor Farjeon:*

SING FOR YOUR SUPPER
OVER THE GARDEN WALL
JOAN'S DOOR
COME CHRISTMAS

*In addition there are twenty poems from her* COLLECTED POEMS *which heretofore has been published only in England.*

# Foreword

Hilaire Belloc once wrote that it is the best of all trades to make songs, and the second best to sing them. I was singing songs before I could write, and even before I could speak, and as soon as I could guide a pencil I began to write them. All told, I have been writing songs for over sixty years, and for at least half of them song-making has been my trade.

By "songs" Hilaire Belloc meant, of course, those poems that are born, as it were, of a tune in the poet's ear. For such poems there seems to be an inevitable melody lying in wait, till somebody comes along to catch it out of the air. It may not happen at once, it may even never happen; but verse has whole regions in which the words and music seem to have come into being together, like twins. The lucky ones quickly found each other in their own time. It is as difficult to think of "Greensleeves" or "Les Lauriers sont coupés" without the tunes that are their birthright, as it is impossible to think of them with any other tunes. No doubt there are numbers of verses still looking for their lost tunes in the places where they were born. The moonstruck region of folk-runes, the golden realm of Elizabethan lyric, the gardens of nursery rhyme, are rich in unmated words and music still undis-covered. But even when the tune of some lilting rhyme has gone astray, we cannot doubt that the poet set down his words with a melody in his ear.

It was in these realms, these gardens, I wandered mostly from the time I could listen and read: in meadows Shakespeare painted with delight, and Herrick pied with daisies, where I heard Blake's lambs bleating and his maids laughing, Nash's cuckoo calling, and Keats's sweet dove grieving; where lovers met their lasses, little boys slept under haycocks, little girls sat on tuffets, and children on May-Day sang the anonymous songs that are almost innocent of meaning, and are so enchanting that they need none.

> "Here we come a-piping,
>  In springtime and in May;
>  Green fruit a-ripening,
>  And Winter fled away.
>  The Queen she sits upon the strand,
>  Fair as lily, white as wand;
>  Seven billows on the sea,
>  Horses riding fast and free,
>  And bells beyond the sand."

Let us not try to explain it. The first lines are as clear as dew, in wording and intention; they are childhood's Open Sesame, to make you come to the door with a penny or a cake. But what horses are suddenly let loose, to canter whither? Upon what nameless sea roll those seven billows, what bells are ringing beyond the mapless sand? Don't let us ask! Ask rather what poor sort of childhood was ours if we never heard them. I have never stopped hearing them, nor ever asked the meaning of any of the lovely loony lines, whose magic of imagery and cadence are childhood's own, before it knows reason. "Be good," said a country nursemaid long ago to a crying child, "be good and I'll give you a Silver-New-Nothing." The child was pacified with wonder. Silver-New-Nothings, those bells beyond the sand—and lavender's blue diddle-diddle, the bailey beareth the bell away, a foolish thing is but a toy, and the cow jumps over the moon.

In my youth I dreamed of being a "real" poet, but halfway through my life the dream died, and whatever figments of it remained went into writing songs and verses for children. From many small books published during the last three decades I have made the present choice, with the addition of some unpublished verses, a few descriptive, but mostly lyrical. Indeed, the result of my gleanings from my nursery-garden is so largely lyrical that it seems to me I have always versified with a tune in my ear. I can hardly remember the time when it did not seem *easier* to me to write in running rhyme than in plodding prose; harder to turn a sod of earth with my spade than to build with sand; *much* harder to model a durable likeness in clay than to shape a little figure out of snow; silver-sand that trickles through the fingers, and snow that melts in the sun.

*Eleanor Farjeon*

# Contents

MEETING MARY                          page 1

SING FOR YOUR SUPPER                      15

OVER THE GARDEN WALL                      81

JOAN'S DOOR                              155

COME CHRISTMAS                          197

ELEANOR FARJEON'S POEMS FOR CHILDREN

# Meeting Mary

A selection of poems from *Collected Poems*
now published in America for the first time

# MEETING MARY

Hard by the Wildbrooks I met Mary,
When berries smelled sweet and hot.
Mary, I fancy, was seven years old,
And I am never mind what.

"What are you getting?" I asked Mary.
"Blackberries. What are you?"
"Toadflax," I answered Mary, "and mushrooms."
"How many mushrooms?" "Two."

"Going to have blackberries stewed for dinner,
Or blackberry jam?" said I.
"Not goin' to have neither," said Mary;
"Goin' to have blackberry pie."

"Aren't you lucky!" I said to Mary.
"And what sort of name have you got?"
"*My* name's Mary," said Mary, "what *your* name?"
I told her never mind what.

"Good-bye, Mary." "Good-bye," said Mary,
And went on picking and eating.
That's all about my meeting with Mary—
It's my favourite sort of meeting.

## MARY'S ONE

*Do you write one every day? said Mary.*
  *Well, I said, I try.*
*Then will you write one for me? said Mary.*
  *That I will, said I.*

I went with Mary to find a ball—
    And we never found it;
To look for a thrush's nest—and all
    We saw were the hedge-leaves round it;

To see a wagtail on a pond—
    But we couldn't catch it;
And a water-lily that grew beyond—
    Too far for us to snatch it;

To watch for rabbits in a grove
    At play on a sandbank sunny—
But I was born as blind as love,
    And never saw one bunny.

After that I wrote Mary one
    In less than half a minute—
And now that Mary's one is done
    I see there's nothing in it.


## SNOW

Oh the falling Snow!
    Oh the falling Snow!
Where does it all come from
Whither does it go?
Never never laughing,
Never never weeping,
Falling in its Sleep,
Forever ever sleeping—
From what Sleep of Heaven
Does it flow, and go
Into what Sleep of Earth,
The falling falling Snow?

## WAVES

There's big waves and little waves,
   Green waves and blue,
Waves you can jump over,
   Waves you dive through,
Waves that rise up
   Like a great water wall,
Waves that swell softly
   And don't break at all,
Waves that can whisper,
   Waves that can roar,
And tiny waves that run at you
   Running on the shore.

## SAND

The Sand is the Sand, till you take it
   And make it
Whatever you fancy—just see
   What things Sand can be!
A castle, a fortress, a wall,
   A tunnel, a ball,
A hole, or a boat, or a seat,
   Or a pudding to eat,
A garden, a churchyard, a hill—
   Sand is just what you will,
Until you've gone home to your tea,
   And the incoming sea
Washes out all the labours you planned again.
   Then, Sand is Sand again.

# YELLOWHAMMER

*Little bit o' bread and NO cheese!*
*Little bit o' bread and NO cheese!*
There it preens its wings, there it sits and sings:
*Little bit o' bread and NO cheese!*
  Yellowhammer, please,
  *Why* don't you like cheese?
*Little bit o' bread and NO cheese!*
  Shall I bring instead
  Butter for your bread?
*Little bit o' bread and NO cheese!*
  Would you like, you funny
  Fellow, jam or honey?
*Little bit o' bread and NO cheese!*
  Yellowhammer, *please,*
  If you won't have cheese,
Tell me what you *do* want?—NO *cheese!*
There the silly thing sits and swings and sings:
*Little bit o' bread and NO cheese!*


# WILDFLOWERS

We mustn't pick the garden flowers
  Because they've got a wall round them,
But wildflowers in the grass are ours
  With woods and meadows all round them.

The buttercups and daisies stand
  And wait for us to play with them,
And primroses on every hand
  Ask us to go away with them.

The bluebell and the daffodil
  Belong to all who feel for them,

The cowslips growing on the hill
   Are yours if you will kneel for them.

The willowherb, the gold kingcup,
   Are his who seeks the brook for them,
And violets are for picking up
   If you will only look for them.

The garden flowers inside the wall
   Belong to him who planted them,
But God once sowed the wildflowers all
   For anyone who wanted them.


## VEGETABLES

The country vegetables scorn
   To lie about in shops,
They stand upright as they were born
   In neatly-patterned crops;

And when you want your dinner you
   Don't buy it from a shelf,
You find a lettuce fresh with dew
   And pull it for yourself;

You pick an apronful of peas
   And shell them on the spot,
You cut a cabbage, if you please,
   To pop into the pot.

The folk who their potatoes buy
   From sacks before they sup,
Miss half of the potato's joy,
   And that's to dig it up.

## FARMS

What jolly things are farms!
  They're many things in one—
I could not count their charms
  From now till set of sun.
They're lambs and sheep in pens,
  They're styes of pigs and sows,
They're yards of cocks and hens,
  They're byres of calves and cows,
They're fields of grass and corn,
  They're gardens with a wall
Where cabbages are born
  And beans and peas and all.
They're dairies clean and cool,
  They're duck-ponds round and green,
They're sheds where every tool
  Of every sort is seen;
They're barns and harness-rooms
  Full of delightful smells,
They're borders full of blooms,
  They're ladders, pumps, and wells,
They're lofts of which one makes
  Great playrooms full of fun,
They're kitchens where the farmwife bakes
Her loaves and pies and little cakes
  And always gives you one.

## ORGAN-GRINDER

When the Organ-Grinder turns his organ-handle
  In the handsome broadways, people often say,
In their easy arm-chairs, "Isn't it a scandal!
Give the fellow sixpence and bid him go away."

When the Organ-Grinder turns his organ-handle
In the narrow alleys where the children play
Girls and boys start dancing, wives their babies dandle,
Saying, "Here's a copper, please don't go away."


## THE FLOWER-SELLER

The Flower-Seller's fat and she wears a big shawl,
    She sits on the kerb with her basket and all,
The wares that she sells are not very dear,
And are always the loveliest things of the year.
        Daffodils in April,
        Purple flags in May,
        Sweet Peas like butterflies
        Upon a summer day,
        Brown leaves in autumn,
        Green leaves in spring,
        And berries in the winter
        When the carol-singers sing.
The Flower-Seller sits with her hands in her lap,
When she's not crying Roses she's taking a nap,
Her bonnet is queer, and she calls you My Dear,
And sells you the loveliest things of the year.


## FOR MARY AND HER KITTEN

        The Kitten's in the Dairy!
          Where's our Mary?
        She isn't in the Kitchen,
        She isn't at her Stitching,
        She isn't at the Weeding,
        The Brewing, or the Kneading!
Mary's in the Garden, walking in a Dream,
Mary's got her Fancies, and the Kitten's got the Cream.

## LIGHT THE LAMPS UP, LAMPLIGHTER!

Light the lamps up, Lamplighter,
    The people are in the street—
        Without a light
        They have no sight,
And where will they plant their feet?
Some will tread in the gutter,
And some in the mud—oh dear!
Light the lamps up, Lamplighter,
Because the night is here.

Light the candles, Grandmother,
The children are going to bed—
        Without a wick
        They'll stumble and stick,
And where will they lay their head?
Some will lie on the staircase,
And some in the hearth—oh dear!
Light the candles, Grandmother,
Because the night is here.

Light the stars up, Gabriel,
The cherubs are out to fly—
        If heaven is blind
        How will they find
Their way across the sky?
Some will splash in the Milky Way,
Or bump on the moon—oh dear!
Light the stars up, Gabriel,
Because the night is here.

## THE NIGHT WILL NEVER STAY

The night will never stay,
The night will still go by,
Though with a million stars
You pin it to the sky;
Though you bind it with the blowing **wind**
And buckle it with the moon,
The night will slip away
Like a sorrow or a tune.


## WHEN JANE GOES TO MARKET

When Jane goes to market she wears a pick gown,
    Her buckles are bigger than any in town;
She's so busy dressing that when she must start
She never remembers the eggs for the mart,
    The eggs for the mart,
    When Jane goes to market,
When Jane goes to market so pretty and smart!

Her cape is of satin, her mittens of lace,
She wears a straw bonnet to shadow her face;
She's so busy tying the strings to her mind
She forgets that she's left all the butter behind,
    The butter behind
    When Jane goes to market,
When Jane goes to market her fortune to find.

When Jane goes to market the gentry all stare,
For Jane is the prettiest country-girl there;
But when the young bucks come to buy of the **belle**
They find they do not come off very well—

They don't come off well
  When Jane goes to market,
When Jane goes to market with nothing to sell!


## THE WAVES OF THE SEA

Don't you go too near the sea,
  The sea is sure to wet you.
Harmless though she seems to be
  The sea's ninth wave will get you!
But I can see the small white waves
  That want to play with me—
They won't do more than wet my feet
  When I go near the sea.

Don't you go too near the sea,
  She does not love a stranger,
Eight untroubled waves has she,
  The ninth is full of danger!
But I can see the smooth blue waves
  That want to play with me—
They won't do more than wet my knees
  When I go near the sea.

Don't you go too near the sea,
  She'll set her waves upon you.
Eight will treat you playfully,
  Until the ninth has won you.
But I can see the big green waves
  That want to play with me—
They won't do more than wet my waist
  When I go near the sea.

Don't you go too near the sea,
  Her ways are full of wonder.
Her first eight waves will leave you free,

Her ninth will take you under!
But I can see the great grey waves
    That want to play with me—
They won't do more than wet my neck
    When I go near the sea.

Don't you go too near the sea—
    O Child, you set me quaking!
Eight have passed you silently,
    And now the ninth is breaking!
I see a wave as high as a wall
    That wants to play with me—
O Mother, O Mother, it's taken me all,
    For I went too near the sea!

## THE WIND

Where the Wind blows
It sows, it sows!
Seed scatters,
Grass grows,
Earth starts,
Water flows,
And Polly's Cheek is like a Rose.

## FOR A DANCE

Round the Maypole dance about,
    Dance your Ribbons in and out;
When they're plaited, then begin
    To dance your Ribbons out and in.
Green and Yellow this way, that way Red and Blue,
Plait the Dance, unplait the Dance, and plait the Dance
    anew!

## THE BIRDS KNOW

The birds know.—You can hear they know,
The eager birds at daybreak; though
The morning is less gold than grey,
And a cold wind still cuts the day,
And skies still look like snow.

The birds their chorus have begun.
No weather now can stop it; none
Can hear them at the early hour
And not foresee the lanes in flower,
Or dream upon the sun.

## STRAWBERRIES

Ripe, ripe Strawberries!
    Who'll buy Strawberries?
Buy my Strawberries red and sweet!
Then your Child can have a treat,
And I'll trudge Home and rest my Feet,
And cry no more in the dusty Street,
    Ripe, ripe Strawberries!
    Who'll buy Strawberries?

# Sing for Your Supper

# SING FOR YOUR SUPPER

Sing for your supper,
  My little lady!
Sing for your supper,
Here, there, and anywhere,
  My little man!
When it comes candletime,
Sing for your supper
  Out of the pan.

Gammon and spinach,
Cream and plum-porridge,
Eggs from the basket,
  Milk from the can,
Sugar and strawberries,
  My little lady,
Pease-pudding hot-and-cold,
  My little man.

Pastries from Cornwall
  Baked by your nanny,
Dumplings from Norfolk
  Boiled by your gran,
Honey from Devonshire
  For a small lady,
Hot-pot from Lancashire
  For a wee man.

Laugh for your breakfast
  Loud as you like to,
Dance for your dinner
  Light as you can,
Last thing at candletime
Sing for your supper,
My little lady,
  My little man!

## THE WILLOW-WREN

*(English Child's Song)*

Rosy Betsy, blue-eyed Milly,
Maidens to the meadows, will ye!
    Blackbird's shout
    Rings round about,
And Jenny Wren is building in the willows.
    Put off your coats of grey and brown,
    Put off the clogs you wear in town,
    Toiling and moiling up and down,
While the wren is building in the willows.

Rosy Betsy, blue-eyed Milly,
Will ye, won't ye, won't ye, will ye?
    Who can stay
    At home all day,
While Jenny Wren is building in the willows?
    Put on your primrose-colored gown,
    Run in your green shoes out of town,
    Run till your tresses tumble down,
Looking for the nest among the willows!

## NINE RED HORSEMEN

*(Mexican Child's Song)*

I saw nine red horsemen ride over the plain,
And each gripped his horse by its long flowing mane.

*Ho-hillo-hillo-hillo-ho!*

Their hair streamed behind them, their eyes were ashine,
They all rode as one man, although they were nine.

*Ho-hillo-hillo-hillo-ho!*

Their spurs clinked and jingled, their laughter was gay,
And in the red sunset they galloped away.

*Ho-hillo-hillo-hillo-ho!*

## BELL-SONG

### *(Welsh Child's Song)*

In the greenwood stands a chapel
Underneath an apple-tree,
In the greenwood stands a chapel
Underneath a yellow apple.
*Ding-dong! ding-dong! ding-dong! ding-dong!*
*Ding-dong, ding-a-ding-a-dong!*

No one goes inside the chapel
Underneath the apple-tree;
No one goes inside the chapel,
No one comes to shake an apple.
*Ding-dong! ding-dong! ding-dong! ding-dong!*
*Ding-dong, ding-a-ding-a-dong!*

But like bells above the chapel
Shakes the yellow apple-tree;
Like sweet bells above the chapel
Shakes the yellow, mellow apple.
*Ding-dong! ding-dong! ding-dong! ding-dong!*
*Ding-dong, ding-a-ding-a-dong!*

## WHEN THE ALMOND BLOSSOMS

### (*Chinese Child's Song*)

When the Almond blossoms,
I and my playfellows
Will float our paper boats
On the yellow stream.
When the Cherry blossoms,
I and my playfellows
Will light our paper lanterns
Under the white bough.

## WHO'LL BUY MY VALLEY LILIES?

### (*Street Child's Song*)

Who'll buy my valley lilies?
Who'll buy my scented gillies?
    All for a little money!
Who'll buy my daffydillies?

Who'll buy my blushing roses
For to delight their noses?
    All for a little money!
Who'll buy my scented posies?

They who buy rings and laces
For their fair hands and faces,
    All for a lot of money,
Yet will not buy such graces.

Who'll buy my valley lilies?
Who'll buy my scented gillies?
    All for a little money!
Who'll buy my daffydillies?

## WHAT SHOULD I SEE?

*(German Child's Song)*

Under the boulders
What should I see
If the King of the Mountain
Came for me?
Gnomes and goblins
Picking for gold:
They'd give and give me
What I could hold!
     But when I returned
     To Motherkin's roof,
     Not a single speck
     Would be there for proof.

Under the water
What should I see
If the Queen of the River
Came for me?
Nis and Nixie
Stringing the pearls:
They'd twist and twist them
Into my curls!
     But when I returned
     To Motherkin's house,
     There wouldn't be one
     To throw to a mouse.

Over the storm-cloud
What should I see
If the wild Wind-Woman
Came for me?
Webs of silver
Above the storm:
She'd weave and weave them
About my form!

But when I returned
To Motherkin's place,
Of all that silver
There'd be no trace.

Over the sun-top
What should I see
If the Lord of Light
Came down for me?
All the diamonds
Of day and night:
He'd heap and heap me
With jewels bright.
But when I returned
To Motherkin's home,
I should go back
As I had come.


## THE LIGHT HEART

*(Italian Child's Song)*

I'd rather be a peasant
Without a care or sorrow
Than wear the Sultan's Crescent,
    Or be a Tartar Khan.
My oxen are the whitest
That till the Tuscan furrow,
My heart, my heart's the lightest
    From Naples to Milan!

I'd rather play with Lisa,
My little peasant-maiden,
Than own the Tower of Pisa
    Or dwell in Peter's Dome.

My lemon-trees are brightest,
My figs the heaviest-laden,
My heart, my heart's the lightest
    From Genoa to Rome!


## FAT HANS SCHNEIDER

### (*Dutch Child's Song*)

Ha, ha, ha! Fat Hans Schneider!
Always drinking Schnapps or cider!
Two round eyes like two full moons,
Two round trousers like balloons,
Two round cheeks like two red cheeses,
Hans goes a-skating whenever it freezes.

Ha, ha, ha! Fat Hans Schneider!
Skating on the Zee of Zuyder
Mynheer Schneider got a fall
And rolled away like a rubber ball.
All through drinking Schnapps of Schiedam,
Hans rolled away like a cheese of Edam!

Ha, ha, ha! Fat Hans Schneider
As he rolled grew wide and wider!
When he reached the tulip-field,
"Oh, what a bulb!" the people squealed.
They planted Hans in their biggest pottery—
He may take a prize, but life's a lottery!

                Ha, ha, ha!
                Fat Hans Schneider!
                Fat Hans Schneider,
                Ha, ha, ha!

## HEY! MY PONY!

*(Tartar Child's Song)*

What will you ride on?
I'll ride a nut-brown pony!
Hempen halter, iron bit,
Round the field I'll ride on it!
   Hey! my nut-brown pony!

What will you ride on?
I'll ride a coal-black pony!
Scarlet saddle, silken reins,
I will cross Sahara's plains.
   Hey! my coal-black pony!

What will you ride on?
I'll ride a snow-white pony!
Silver bridle, golden girth,
I will travel round the earth.
   Hey! My snow-white pony!

## BRAVERY

*(Small Child's Song)*

The cow in the meadow
  Looks sideways at me—
  But what do I care?
  With my chin in the air,
I stare at the stile,
  Or a cloud, or a tree,
When the cow in the meadow
  Looks sideways at me.

The cow in the meadow
　　Is not more than three,
　　And you're not very bold
　　When you aren't very old,
So I mustn't alarm her—
　　She's *timid*, you see,
And that's why she always
　　Looks sideways at me.

She gives me my milk
　　And my butter for tea.
　　"*Git* on!" says John,
　　And at once she gits on—
And I stick to the footpath
　　As brave as can be,
When the cow in the meadow
　　Looks sideways at me.


## OL' RED THIEF

Who's dat a-barkin',
Who's dat a-barkin',
Who's dat a-barkin'
　　　　　so shrill?
Guess it's Brudder Fox,
Ol' Brudder Fox,
Carryin' de lil white lamb
　　　　　　　a-way,
Way over de hill.
　　Nuffin' but a Big Gun
　　Ain't gwine ter kill
　　Dat Ol' Red Thief
　　W'at hide um in de hill!

Who's dat a-squealin',
Who's dat a-squealin',
Who's dat a-squealin'
         so shrill?
Guess it's Mammy Ewe,
Po' Mammy Ewe,
Cryin' fer her lil white lamb,
                 a-way,
Way over de hill.
     Who'll get a Big Gun
     An' go fer to kill
     Dat Ol' Red Thief
     W'at hide um in de hill!

Who's dat a-laffin',
Who's dat a-laffin',
Who's dat a-laffin'
         so shrill?
Guess it's Mister Man,
Big Mister Man,
Carryin' de lil white lamb
                 a-way,
Way back from de hill,
     Mister Man's Big Gun
     Done gwine kill
     Dat Ol' Red Thief
     W'at hide um in de hill!

## THE PEDDLER

*(Ragamuffin's Song)*

There was an old Peddler
Who lived on the road,
With a load
On his back,

And a pack
On his moke,
And a joke
On his lips.
He ate fish and chips
From a big paper bag,
His coat was a rag,
Upon his left foot
He wore a black boot,
On his right
A white
Shoe—
Tooralee! tooraloo!
The moke went behind and the peddler before,
And that's all about 'em, so don't ask for more.


## EM

Em with her basket
   Goes all down the hedges,
Picking up little things
   Nearest the edges.
All through the seasons
   She trots at her task—it
Takes a full year to fill
   Em's wicker basket.
Now a wild strawberry
   Spoiled by the weather,
Now a white violet,
   Now a blue feather,
Knots of tight cobnuts
   Before they have ripened,
Here a round pebble and
   There a clay pipe-end,
Now the white dead-nettle's
   Secret of honey,

Once a black threepenny,
  Somebody's money,
Smooth glossy rose-hips
  Brighter than cherries,
Green-beaded, red-beaded,
  Not-yet-black-berries,
Such a brown toadstool
  Tougher than leather,
Such soft grey fleece from some
  Long-gone-by wether—
Oh, what a business
  This, of the hedges!
Picking and gathering
  All down the edges,
Filling her basket
  And full of soft chatter,
What does Em do with it?
  What does it matter?


## NAN

**It's**
  Nan! Nan! where have you got to?
  Nan! Nan! you know it's not right!
  Now then, you *are* to! Now then, you're *not* to!
  That's how it is from morning to night.

  Just whatever you've set your heart on
  They put a stop to, I don't know why.
  There's a new black calf been born in the barton,
  And ten pigwiggins in Grunter's sty—

**But it's**
  Nan! Nan! where are you going?
  Nan! Nan! where have you been?
  And the game is up if they know you're knowing
  Who is calling and what they mean.

There's a pheasant's clutch hid under the bracken,
And Tib's got her kittens behind the shed,
Two grey tabbies, a white-and-black 'un,
A tortoiseshell, and a gold-and-red.

And it's
   Nan! Nan! what are you doing?
   Nan! Nan! what have you done?
   Then you know there is trouble brewing,
   And you stop your ears and begin to run.

There's newts in the ditch below the alder,
And a squirrel's nest in the round-oak tree—
You never saw bulgier eyes or balder
Babies than squirrel's baby-three.

Then it's
   Torn your frock? (Huh! it's only cotton!)
   *Look* at your hands! you *are* a sight!—
   They've simply forgotten. They've simply *forgotten*,
   And that's how it is from morning to night.


## DAVID

Yes, David puts his toys away,
And washes behind his ears,
   If he climbs a tree
   And barks his knee
He doesn't resort to tears;
He never gives girls and boys away,
He has the politest tones,
In fact, he is a *good* little boy,
   But he *will—throw—stones*.

   He throws them at the window-panes,
   He throws them at the water,

He throws them at his Aunty Jane's
Inoffensive daughter,
He throws them for old Rover to
Bring them back again like treasure,
He throws them Over, At, and Through,
For nothing else but pleasure;
He shies at acorns, conkers, cones,
And always scores a single,
He chucks his stones at other stones
Lying on the shingle,
He aims at stumps and sitting hens,
He marks down running rabbits—
It's just another of you men's
Incalculable habits.

He has no motive deep and dark,
That isn't it a bit, it
Is: that when David spies his mark
He *simply—has—*to hit it.

David gives his things away,
And brushes his teeth at night,
    He seldom fails
    To clean his nails,
And he gets his homework right,
And everybody brings away
The same report with groans:
"David *is* a good little boy,
    But he *does—throw—stones!*"

## GRISELDA

Griselda is greedy, I'm sorry to say.
She isn't contented with four meals a day,
Like breakfast and dinner and supper and tea
(I've had to put tea after supper—you see
                    *Why*, don't you?)
Griselda is greedy as greedy can be.

    She snoops about the larder
    For sundry small supplies,
    She breaks the little crusty bits
    Off rims of apple pies,
    She pokes the roast-potato-dish
    When Sunday dinner's done,
    And if there are two left in it
    Griselda snitches one;
    Cold chicken and cold cauliflower
    She pulls in little chunks—
And when Cook calls:
        "What *are* you doing there?"
        Griselda bunks.

Griselda is greedy. Well, that's how she feels,
She simply can't help eating in-between meals,
And always forgets what it's leading to, though
The Doctor has frequently told her: "You know
                    Why, *don't* you?"
When the stomach-ache starts and Griselda says:
    "Oh."

    She slips down to the dining-room
    When every one's in bed,
    For cheese-rind on the supper-tray,
    And buttered crusts of bread,
    A biscuit from the biscuit-box,
    Lump sugar from the bowl,

A gherkin from the pickle-jar,
Are all Griselda's toll;
She tastes the salted almonds,
And she tries the candied fruit—
And when Dad shouts:
      "Who *is* it down below?"
      Griselda scoots.

Griselda is greedy. Her relatives scold,
And tell her how sorry she'll be when she's old,
She will lose her complexion, she's sure to grow fat,
She will spoil her inside—does she know what she's at?
               (Why *do* they?)
*Some* people *are* greedy. Leave it at that.


## TOM

Tom wonders when it comes about
That people's minds turn inside out
As they grow up. He knows they do,
Because they aren't like him and you.

They do not *like* sardines with jam,
They never *want* to try to dam
The brook with mud and stones, and stay
Past tea-time, doing it all day.

They stick to stuffy rooms, although
They might take cake and cheese and go
Off to the hollow oak, and light
A fire outside, and stay all night.

They keep their boots on all the time,
You never, *never* see them climb
The workman's ladder to the roof.
They've changed their minds, and that's the proof.

They *must* have wanted once to do
That sort of thing like him and you.
How dreadful if it comes about
That Tom turns *his* mind inside out!

## FRED

Fred likes creatures,
And has a lot of 'em.
Bees don't sting him,
He's got a pot of 'em,
Little round velvety bodies they are
Making honey in Fred's jam-jar.

Fred likes creatures.
Hedgehogs don't prickle him,
They flatten their quills
And scarcely tickle him,
But lie with their pointed snouts on his palm,
And their beady eyes are perfectly calm.

Fred likes creatures.
The nestling fallen out
Of the tree-top
With magpie callin' out
*Where? where? where?* contented lingers
In the round nest of Fred's thick fingers.

Fred likes creatures.
Nothing's queer to him,
Ferrets, tortoises,
Newts are dear to him.
The lost wild rabbit comes to his hand
As to a burrow in friendly land.

Fred *eats* rabbit
Like any glutton, too,
Fred eats chicken
And beef and mutton too.
Moral? None. No more to be said
Than Fred likes creatures, and creatures like Fred.


## MINNIE

Minnie can't make her mind up,
Minnie can't make up her mind!
    They ask her at tea,
    "Well, what shall it be?"
    And Minnie says, "Oh,
    Muffins, please! no,
    Sandwiches—yes,
    Please, egg-and-cress—
    I mean a jam one,
    Or is there a ham one,
Or is there another kind?
    *Never* mind!
        Cake
    Is what I will take,
The sort with the citron-rind,
    Or p'r'aps the iced one—
    Or is there a spiced one,
Or is there the currant kind?"
    When tea is done
    She hasn't begun,
She's always the one behind,
Because she can't make her mind up,
Minnie *can't* make up her mind!

## PETER

It's all very well, said Peter to Mike,
To say Be brave! but how would you like
When the water runs out with a *glug-glug-glug,*
How would *you* like to be sucked down the Plug?

Next year, when I am as big as you,
I'll sit it out to the finish too,
See if I don't! and let it run
Away till the very last drop is done.

And the squelchy sound it makes in the hole
Won't bother me then, upon my soul!
But this year it's all very well to sneer—
Just you remember yourself last year.

You've *forgot* how the hole gets bigger and bigger
Till it's bigger around than your own figure!
It's so long ago, you've *forgot* what it's like,
*That's* what it is, said Peter to Mike.

And I *will* get out when the water goes *glug!*
And I *won't* be sucked down the Bathroom Plug!


## NED

It's a singular thing that Ned
Can't be got out of bed.
        When the sun comes round
        He is sleeping sound
With the blankets over his head.

They tell him to shunt,
And he gives a grunt,
And burrows a little deeper—
He's a trial to them
At eight a.m.,
When Ned is a non-stop sleeper.
Oh, the snuggly bits
Where the pillow fits
Into his cheek and neck!
Oh, the beautiful heat
Stored under the sheet
Which the breakfast-bell will wreck!
Oh, the snoozly-oozly feel
He feels from head to heel,
When to get out of bed
Is worse to Ned
Than missing his morning meal!

*But*

It's a singular thing that Ned,
After the sun is dead
And the moon's come round,
Is not to be found,
And can't be got into bed!

## JENNY

Her aunties trains of satin don
When going to a ball—
But Jenny puts the bath-towel on
And trails it down the hall.

There's diamonds on her mother's gown,
And rubies in her hair—
But Jenny has a cake-tin crown
And curtain-ring to wear.

Her sister at the dance prefers
Some other lady's dress—
But Jenny's satisfied with hers,
For *she's a real* Princess!


## DOG

Whether I'm Alsatian,
Dachshund or Dalmatian,
Or any one among the Terrier crew,
However brief you've known me,
As long as you will own me
I'm Dog, that's all, my Master, Dog to you.

If you like a Setter
Or a Spaniel better,
Aberdeen or Airdale—some folk do—
Whatever breed you name me,
As long as you will claim me
I'm yours for life, my Master, Dog to you.

I'll love you, Cairn or Collie,
Beyond the point of folly,
And if I'm Mongrel, love you just as true;
Kick me or caress me,
As long as you possess me
I'm yours till death, my Master, Dog to you.

For you, I'll be so knowing!
I'll whimper at your going,
And at your coming, wag myself in two!
Trust you while I tease you,
Pester you to please you,
*Your* Dog, that's all, Master, Dog to you.

## BOASTING

I like biscuit,
I like bones,
I like bread and cake and scones.

I can bay
And I can bark,
I can bite and make my mark.

I can beg,
And I can bury
What I'm given deep down, very.

I can bounce
And I can bound
After balls he throws around.

I can bear,
And I can bring
Anything and everything.

I can be
A sorry beast
When my master loves me least—

When my master loves me most,
Can't I brag!
And can't I boast!


## CAT!

*Cat!*
Scat!
Atter her, atter her,

Sleeky flatterer,
Spitfire chatterer,
Scatter her, scatter her
    Off her mat!
    *Wuff!*
    *Wuff!*
    Treat her rough!
Git her, git her,
Whiskery spitter!
Catch her, catch her,
Green-eyed scratcher!
    Slathery
    Slithery
    Hisser,
    Don't miss her!
Run till you're dithery,
    Hithery
    Thithery!
    *Pfitts! pfitts!*
    How she spits!
    *Spitch! spatch!*
    Can't she scratch!

Scritching the bark
Of the sycamore-tree,
She's reached her ark
And's hissing at me
    *Pfitts! pfitts!*
    *Wuff! wuff!*
    Scat,
    Cat!
    That's
    *That!*

## FRIEND OR FOE?

Is he Friend or is he Foe?
When my Master speaks, I'll know.

If he's Friend, I'll quiet stand,
Wag my tail, and lick his hand.

If he's Foe, I'll snarl and growl,
For he must be very foul.

If he's Friend, I'll do my best
To put paws upon his chest.

If he's Foe, I'll bare my teeth
And find out what lies beneath.

I'll accept him to the end,
If he is my Master's Friend.

If he's Foe, before I've done
I will have him on the run.

Is he Friend, or is he Foe?
Master, speak! and I shall know.

## INSIDE

A bellyful and the fire,
And him in his old suit,
And me with my heart's desire,
My head across his foot.

And I doze. And he reads.
And the clock ticks slow.

And, though he never heeds,
He knows, and I know.

Presently, without look,
His hand will feel to tug
My ear, his eyes on book,
Mine upon the rug.


## OUTSIDE

He's pulling on his boots!
He's going out again—
Out to the world of roots,
The whipping wind and rain,
The stinging sun that tells
On bristles and in blood,
Out to the place of smells,
And things that move, and mud;
Out where, to run a race,
Is not to hit a wall;
Out to the time of chase!
Will he whistle and call?
He's looking for his stick,
He's— Hark! his glorious shout!
I'm coming quick-quick-quick!
We're going out! We're *Out.*


## HEEL

The sun inside me lights a flame,
The wind says everything I feel.
Life is my tremendous game!
Race? Hunt? Fight? Bark? Gobble? Steal?—
Quietly, he says my name
In *that* voice. And I come to heel.

## LEAD

Not the lead, please, not the lead!
I'll behave myself indeed!
See me plead with all my eyes,
*Not* the lead.

I will try, so hard I'll try,
On our ramble not to fly
At my sly sleek mewing black
Enemy:

Not to enter into fight
With Old Bandy-Legs, whose bite
Hangs on tight, as soon as he
Heaves in sight.

Not to run at horses' feet,
Or at children whom we meet,
Or the fleet of motor-cars
In the street.

Or at silly sheep in lanes,
Or through open window-panes,
Or at trains, or over walls,
Or down drains.

Not the lead, please, not the lead!
Let your humble serf indeed
Be your freedman for to-day—
*Not* the lead!

## KENNEL

Kennel's my castle
Where I am king.
He can't come in it,
No such thing.

Shadow in sun,
Shelter in rain,
Where I keep office
In collar and chain.

Kennel's my castle
Where I am law.
Servants scour it
And bring me straw.

In its darkness,
Unseen, unsought,
I gnaw my bone.
And gnaw my thought.

Kennel's my castle
Where I am stuck.
*He* can't come in it,
No such luck.


## VET

Must we go inside there?
Must we go in there?
Always something *diff'rent*
In the fellow's air.

Yes, I will stand quiet,
I will stand quite still,
S'long as you don't leave me
Be myself I will.
Fellow's got good fingers,
Firm and kind and quick!
Over? Can we go now?
No, I wasn't sick.
No, I didn't mind it.
Hold me, hug me, do!
No, I didn't feel it.
I was looking at you.


## MOON

Who knows why I stand and bay at her?
Who knows what I have to say at her?
　　　　Even not I.
Only, when she stays and stares at me,
Only, when her white eye glares at me,
　　　　I give cry—
　　　　　　*Hollow! hollow!*
There's a scent I'd fain and cannot follow.

Did she ever lead us runningly
Over height and hillock cunningly
　　　　Time ago?
Were there horns that called us thrillingly,
Fled we on their echoes willingly?
　　　　I but know
　　　　　　*Hollow! hollow!*
There's a scent I'd fain and cannot follow.

Leagues of silver hill-top flowingly
Stretching. Knowingly, unknowingly,
　　　　Antlered heads

Lifting frighted, bending browsingly.
Her voice, *Her Voice* ringing rousingly
                Round our sheds—

                                *Hollow! hollow!*
There's a scent I'd fain and cannot follow.

Whitened arrows wing their mark again!
Light in dark again! light in dark again!
                I give cry!
*Io! Io!* I'll have say at her!
Who knows, who knows why I bay at her?
                Even not I.
                                *Hollow! hollow!*
O the scent I'd fain, and cannot, follow.


## WOLF!

When you think me dreaming, chin on paws,
And a shiver steals along my spine,
And my sleep is shaken by a whine,—
What's the cause, my master, what's the cause?

I am no more housed inside a box,
I in heat or snow am on the track,
I am hunting with the hunting-pack—
Not the fox, my master, not the fox!

Our primeval quarry ranked above
Anything within the four-foot plan
When I ran upon the heels of man—
Not for love, my master, not for love.

Dreaming, with a dread you cannot see,
In the leash of unremembered laws—
Wake me! I am fearful, chin on claws,
Not of You, my master, but of Me.

### RATS!

**Who** said *Rats!*
         and laughed,
And pulled my ears,
And said:
        *I only chaffed,*
*But when he hears*
Rats, boy! *see him jump*
*And hear him bark!*
*Thump tail, crosspatch, thump—*
*It was a lark.*

Oh yes, *I* dare say!
A lark for some—
Cheating one for play,
Thinking it rum
To make a dog a fool!
Hasn't one got
Feelings? Oh, I'm quite cool;
No, I am not
Sulking. Only, I'm through.
I've paid your price,
I know your game, and you
Don't catch me twice.
So just go back and grease
Those cricket-bats,
And leave a dog in peace. . . .
*Wuff!*
        Who said *RATS?*

## BLISS

Let me fetch sticks,
Let me fetch stones,
Throw me your bones,
Teach me your tricks.

When you go ride,
Let me go run,
You in the sun,
Me at your side;

When you go swim,
Let me go too
Both lost in blue
Up to the brim;

Let me do this,
Let me do that—
What you are at,
That is my bliss.


## NOTHING

He's gone—
          and there is nothing.
Kind tones
       are nothing,
Butcher's bones
         are nothing,
The next-door cat
        is nothing,
Even his empty glove and hat
            are nothing,

The fighters in the street
                    are nothing,
Friends, foes, and meat
                    all nothing, nothing, nothing—
He's gone,
          and I am nothing.


## EPITAPH

What is this Stone he's laid upon my bones
For whom I fetched and carried endless stones?
Wait, Master, wait a little. When we meet
You'll know me by my Stone, laid at your feet.


## SCHOOL-BELL

    Nine-o'clock Bell!
    Nine-o'clock Bell!
All the small children and big ones as well,
Pulling their stockings up, snatching their hats,
Cheeking and grumbling and giving back-chats,
Laughing and quarreling, dropping their things,
These at a snail's pace and those upon wings,
Lagging behind a bit, running ahead,
Waiting at corners for lights to turn red,
        Some of them scurrying,
        Others not worrying,
Carelessly trudging or anxiously hurrying,
All through the streets they are coming pell-mell
        At the Nine-o'clock
            Nine-o'clock
            Nine-o'clock
                    Bell!

## CLASS-ROOM

What sort of things are seen in the class-room?
      Blackboards and benches,
      Small lads and wenches.
      Inkstains and pencils,
      Pictures and stencils,
      Teachers and visitors,
      Board-school inquisitors,
      Flowers in gay bunches,
      And paper-bag lunches.

What sort of sounds are heard in the class-room?
      Voices reciting,
      Pens busy writing,
      Slate-pencils squeaking,
      Shouting and speaking,
      Pushing and shuffling
      And shoving and scuffling,
      Teacher's bell ringing,
      And little ones singing.

Call Over! Call Over! Come on, don't fall over!
Twelve o'clock! All over! Out of the class-room!

## ALPHABET

One letter stands for Alphabet,
    And Alphabet stands for all.
There's six-and-twenty in the set
    By which we stand or fall.
And most of us know in our head
Their rightful order, A to Z.

But when we take the Alphabet
      To pieces, and spell words,
The little letters, all upset,
      Fly anywhere, like birds.
Why, ALPHABET itself gets mixed,
And when you spell it, comes unfixed.

For then L follows after A,
      And H comes after P,
And T turns tail and runs away
      To hob-a-nob with E.
You all can *say* your Alphabet—
But, children, can you spell it yet?

## KNOWLEDGE

Your mind is a meadow
To plant for your needs;
You are the farmer,
With knowledge for seeds.

Don't leave your meadow
Unplanted and bare,
Sow it with knowledge
And tend it with care.

Who'd be a know-nothing
When he might grow
The seed of the knowledge
Of stars and of snow;

The science of numbers,
The stories of time.
The magic of music,
The secrets of rhyme?

Don't be a know-nothing!
Plant in the spring,
And see what a harvest
The summer will bring.


## BOOKS

What worlds of wonder are our books!
As one opens them and looks,
New ideas and people rise
In our fancies and our eyes.

The room we sit in melts away,
And we find ourselves at play
With some one who, before the end,
May become our chosen friend.

Or we sail along the page
To some other land or age.
*Here's* our body in the chair,
But our mind is over *there*.

Each book is a magic box
Which with a touch a child unlocks.
In between their outside covers
Books hold all things for their lovers.


## HISTORY

All down the ages
Like a great tide,
Commoners walking
Where noblemen ride,

Now in the sunshine
And now in the shade,
People move onward
While History's made.

Churchmen make churches
And Lawyers make codes,
Builders make cities
And Romans make roads,
Soldiers make battles,
And Merchants make trade,
And people make changes
While History's made.

Craftsmen and Artists
Make manifold things,
Rulers make nations,
And nations make kings—
All down the ages
In great cavalcade,
People move onward,
And History's made.

## GEOGRAPHY

Islands and peninsulas, continents and capes,
Dromedaries, cassowaries, elephants and apes,
Rivers, lakes and waterfalls, whirlpools and the sea,
Valley-beds and mountain-tops—are all Geography!

The capitals of Europe with so many curious names,
The North Pole and the South Pole and Vesuvius in flames,
Rice-fields, ice-fields, cotton-fields, fields of maize and tea,
The Equator and the Hemispheres—are all Geography!

The very streets I live in, and the meadows where I play,
Are just as much Geography as countries far away,
Where yellow girls and coffee boys are learning about *me*,
The little white-skinned stranger who is in Geography!

## NUMBERS

There are hundreds of Numbers. They mount up so high,
That if you could count every star in the sky
From the Tail of the Bear to the Waterman's Hat,
There still would be even more Numbers than that!

There are thousands of Numbers. So many there be,
That if you could count every drop in the sea
From the Mexican Gulf to the Lincolnshire Flat,
There still would be even more Numbers than that!

There are millions of Numbers. So many to spare,
That if you could count every insect in air,
The moth, the mosquito, the bee and the gnat,
There still would be even more Numbers than that!

There's no end to Numbers! But don't be afraid!
There only are ten out of which they are made,
Learn from Nought up to Nine, and the rest will come pat,
For the numbers of Numbers all come out of that!

## INDIA-RUBBER

My india-rubber is the friend
    Who causes faults to fade;
His only purpose is to mend
    Mistakes my pencil made.
The word that has been wrongly spelt,
    The drawing badly done,
Under my india-rubber melt
    Like snowflakes in the sun.
And when my hardest sums begin
    To fill my mind with doubt—
Before my teacher rubs it in,
    Quick, quick! I'll rub them out!

## ENGLISH

As gardens grow with flowers
English grows with words,
Words that have secret powers,
Words that give joy like birds.

Some of the words you say,
Both in and out of school,
Are brighter than the day,
And deeper than a pool.

Some words there are that dance,
Some words there are that sigh,
The fool's words come by chance,
The poet's to heaven fly.

When you are grown, your tongue
Should give the joys of birds;
Get while you are young
The gift of English words.

## LATIN

When Julius Caesar was a child
In Rome, the same things drove him wild
    As now in England fidget us.
He blubbered in the Latin tongue:
"*Mater*, a naughty *Apis* stung
    Me here, upon the *Digitus!*"
(By which he meant: "A naughty Bee
Has stung my finger, Mother, see!")

His Mater took him on her knees,
And cooed: "Those horrid little Bees!
    Now why did Jove invent 'em?"
And then she calmed her *Filius*
And put upon his *Digitus*
    A soothing *Unguentum*.
(Which means, she smeared an Ointment on
The finger of her little son.)

At tea, to make her Julius well,
She gave him *Panis*, spread with *Mel*—
    (And if you think that's funny,
It only means *your* Mother might
Console you for an insect-bite
    At tea with Bread-and-Honey).
Now, Honey's such a pleasant thing
He quite forgot his Apis sting.

Though Julius Caesar lived in Rome,
And you inside a British home,
    You're very like that brat in
The things he said when he was young,
Though you speak in the English tongue,
    And Julius spoke in Latin.
So when you say a Latin word,
That is the one which Caesar heard.

## FRENCH

Isn't it strange
That in Paris
You are Vous
And Moi is Me,
And No and Yes
Are Non and Oui!

Isn't it odd
That in Bordeaux
Bread is Pain
And Water Eau,
And Good and Fair
Are Bon and Beau!

Isn't it queer
That in Calais
French *isn't* French,
And *is* Français!
What sort of French
Can that be, pray?

## VERBS

Nouns are the things I see and touch,
My Cake, my Mother, and my Ball;
I like some Nouns very much,
Though some I do not like at all.

Verbs are the things I do, and make,
And feel, in one way or another.
Thanks to Verbs, I *eat* my Cake,
And *throw* my Ball, and *hug* my Mother.

Yet Verbs, which make me laugh and play,
Can also make me cry and fall,
And *tease* my Mother every day,
And *spoil* my Cake, and *lose* my Ball!


## ORNITHOLOGY

What's ORNITHOLOGY? Pray can you tell?
It's hard to pronounce and it's harder to spell—
Yet that's what you're learning whenever you care
To study the Birds of the Earth, Sea and Air.
       There's a long word
       To stand for a Bird!
For a Lark or a Sparrow its length is absurd!
Eagles and Ostriches need no apology
If you should label them as ORNITHOLOGY!
       But how can it fit
       The tiny Tom-Tit?
       The Finch
Wants a word that's no more than an inch!
Yet all of the Birds of the East and the West,
Whatever they be, and wherever they nest—
       The Vulture—the Hen—
       The Flamingo—the Wren—
       The Dove—the Canary—
       The queer Cassowary—
The Thrush on the bough, and the Duck in the pool—
They are all ORNITHOLOGY when you're in School!

## MUSIC

Can you dance?
I love to dance!
Music is my happy chance.
Music playing
In the street
Gets into
My hands and feet.

Can you sing?
I love to sing!
Music, like a bird in Spring,
With a gold
And silver note
Gets into
My heart and throat.

Can you play?
I'd love to play!
Practise music every day—
Then you'll give
The world a chance
To dance and sing,
To sing and dance.


## POETRY

What is Poetry? Who knows?
Not a rose, but the scent of the rose;
Not the sky, but the light in the sky;
Not the fly, but the gleam of the fly;
Not the sea, but the sound of the sea;
Not myself, but what makes me
See, hear, and feel something that prose
Cannot: and what it is, who knows?

## DANCING

A hop, a skip, and off you go!
Happy heart and merry toe,
Up-and-down and in-and-out,
This way, that way, round about!
Bend like grasses in the breeze,
Wave your arms like wind-blown trees,
Dart like swallows, glide like fish,
Dance like anything you wish.
Soundless as the snowflakes white,
Swift as shooting-stars at night,
Nimble as a goblin elf,
Dance, dance, and be yourself,
Stately, sprightly, so and so,
    Quick and slow,
    To and fro,
Kicking high and jumping low,
A skip, a hop, and off you go!


## TEACHER

Teacher's tall and Teacher's short,
Teacher is of every sort,
Teacher's dark and Teacher's fair,
Teacher has all kinds of hair.

Teacher's dressed in blues and browns,
Teacher smiles and Teacher frowns,
Teacher plays all sorts of games,
Teacher knows us by our names.

Teacher has a name as well,
Teacher is Miss Jones, Miss Bell,
Miss MacAlister, Miss Ryan,
Mrs. Dean, and Miss O'Brien.

Teacher comes from Scotland, Wales,
Cornwall, and the Yorkshire Dales,
From the Stafford Pottery Towns,
London, and the Sussex Downs.

Yet no matter what her name,
Or her place, it's just the same—
Any one who wants to reach her
Only has to say, "Please, Teacher!"


## JABBERING IN SCHOOL

Was that me jabbering?
I expect it was.
It's no *use* explaining
Why and because;
When you've been jabbering
Teacher doesn't *try*
To take any interest
In because and why.
I might have seen a heron
Flying in the sun,
Or been telling Jeanie
Her pinny was undone,
I might have been noticing
Something dark and dire,
Like lions in the playground,
Or the curtains on fire,
I might have had a stomach-ache—
Oh, there might have been
Lots of reasons why I
Was jabbering with Jean.
But it's *no* use explaining
Why and because.
Was that me jabbering?
I expect it was.

## QUESTIONS

The *Questions* they ask!
It's a terrible task
To answer them right!
Although you are quite
Sure you know what to say when the questions are set,
As soon as you're asked them, you seem to forget.

Who *was* Francis Drake?
And where *do* they make
The very best Knives?
Who *were* the Six Wives
Of Henry the Eighth? Why *are* Mites in Cheese?
And what *is* the French for "Some more if you please"?

Where *is* Timbuctoo?
What *did* Nero do?
What Moor is in Devon?
What's Five and Eleven?
And who was the first man to reach the North Pole?
And what was a Coalmine before it was Coal?

Sometimes I say
It right, right away!
Other times—oh,
I just "sort of" know:
But most of the times when the Questions are set,
As soon as I'm asked them, I seem to forget!

## YAWNING

Sometimes—I'm sorry—but sometimes,
Sometimes, yes, sometimes I'm bored.
It may be because I'm an idiot;
It may be because I'm floored;

It may be because it is raining,
It may be because it is hot,
It may be because I have eaten
Too much, or because I have not.

But sometimes I *cannot* help yawning
(I'm sorry!) the whole morning through—
And when Teacher's turning her back on us,
It may be that she's yawning too.


## RULES

All schools
Have rules
Even those without 'em.
It's the rule of those schools
To have no rules,
That's all there is about 'em.


## ZODIAC

What are the signs of Zodiac,
Marked in stars on Heaven's track?

The Water-Carrier bears on high
His jar in January's sky.

February brings a pair
Of Fish to swim in dark blue air.

In March a hornèd Ram doth run
Between the visits of the sun.

April rides upon a Bull
Vigorous and beautiful.

The Twins we call the Gemini
May-month cradles in the sky.

In June the Crab goes crawling o'er
The spaces of the heavenly shore.

Where the Crab no longer creeps,
In July the Lion leaps.

Through August nights, like daisy-laden
Meadows, walks a Vestal Maiden.

September, though it blow big gales,
Holds aloft a pair of Scales.

On October's map is shown
A star-bespangled Scorpion.

In November, kneeling low,
See, the Archer bends his bow.

December's frolic is a Goat
Bleating in his starry throat.

These are the signs of Zodiac,
Marking time on Heaven's track.

## UNIVERSE

The Universe is all the skies
Reaching far beyond your eyes.

The Universe is all the seas
Spreading in unseen degrees.

The Universe is all the earth
Besides the spot that gave you birth.

If you can with your small eye
Know one star in all the sky:

If, of all the seas there be,
From one beach you know the sea:

If, of all the land on earth,
You can know one meadow's worth:

You might do a great deal worse
To understand the Universe.

## NEWS! NEWS!

News! news! I bring you good news!
What will you give me, good wife, for good news!
　A cake or a groat,
　A staff or a coat,
Or a pair of your castaway shoes—for my news!
I went through the lowland
Upon the New Year.
And saw the first aconite

Shining so clear.
   Let the day blow
   With sleet and with snow,
   There's life in the lowland
   Upon the New Year!

I went round the upland
Upon the New Year,
And heard the first bleating
A-calling so clear.
   Let the night fall
   Hoar-frost and all,
   There's life on the upland,
   God bless the New Year!
News! news! I come with good news!
What will you give me, for good news?
   A bench by your fire,
   A bed in your byre,
And a bowl when your old woman brews, for my news!


### THIS YEAR—NEXT YEAR

I've a field with nothing in it
But grass and nettles. Wait a minute!
Wait until my orchard comes,
With apples, cherries, pears and plums,
A greengage and a walnut tree!
By next spring my field will be
A dancing sight! In skirts of white
Little trees will stand upright,
Balanced on one slender limb
Like ballet-maidens, while the rim
Of petticoats a-flutter there
Hide the other toe-in-air.

I've a pond with nothing in it
But clay and duckweed. Wait a minute!
Wait till my blue iris peers
On her image through her spears,
Till my kingcups spread a ring
Bright as sunshine round the spring,
And upon the coverlet
Of their broad green leaves are set
Lilies ivory and gold.
Long before next summer's old,
Bullrush in the water-bed
Will wear a busby on his head.

*And if all my dreams fall flat,*
*If things don't look quite like that*
*Next year—this year, anyhow,*
*That's the way I see them now!*


## JOLLY MARCH WIND

Jolly March Wind
Blows in the street,
The street that was
So quiet and neat,
Each iron gate
Standing so still,
Curtains hung straight
At each window-sill.
　　　　But now—
The dust is whirling!
Chimneysmoke's twirling!
Gates are banging!
Curtains are hanging
　　　　All anyhow!

Prim Miss Muffin
Is pantin' and puffin',
Her petticoat's tossed
And her hair-ribbon lost!
Old Mr. Wrangle
Is cutting a caper
After his paper,
 An absolute wreck,
With his scarf in a tangle
 All round his neck!
But Jimmy and Jenny
Scream with delight,
  As hither
  And thither,
Just like a kite,
  Tumbled,
  And rumpled,
  Untidy,
  Unpinned,
They're blown home to dinner
By jolly March Wind!


## FIRST GATHERING

Child, take your basket down,
Go and find spring,
Earth has not lost her brown
Nor wind his sting,
But in the morning
The thrush and the blackbird
Sing to the sleeping town,
And to the waking woods
Sing:
  take your basket down,
Go and find spring!

Now where the ground was bare
Only last week,
Now where the flower was rare
And the hedge bleak,
Reach for the catkin
And stoop for the primrose,
Seek, if you want your share
Of the first gathering,
Seek,
    where the ground was bare
Only last week.

## MAY MEADOWS

Now May has drawn her meadows up
To meet the knees of kine,
The goblet of the buttercup
Is bright as golden wine.

And where she sets her pasture-lands
With silver daisy-bud,
In tallest grass the red cow stands
Slow-chewing her sweet cud.

The rich green hedge that runs its way
Round England, daily weaves
The rosy may, the pearly may,
Among its deepening leaves.

The swallows like dark comets, in
Bewildering unrest,
Seeking the rising may-flies spin,
To feed the cheeping nest.

Oh time of leisurely content
Amid the shadowed grass!

Oh time so swiftly, swiftly spent
In heaven's shining glass!

Betwixt the wings that fly the steep,
And the earth-loving herds,
As slow as cattle I would keep
The hours, as swift as birds!


## MIDSUMMER EVE

On Midsummer Eve
They used to believe
That elves were about,
And fairies came out,
And witches on brooms,
And wraiths from their tombs,
And goblin and sprite
Made havoc all night.
And Annie, all day
So safe at her play,
Kept at home on
The Eve of St. John.
Her Granny she telled her
The scent of the elder
Possessed a strange charm
To do her some harm.
It might be if she
To the old elder-tree
Went out in the dark
The fairies to mark,
The old Elder-Mother
By some means or other
Would steal her for ever,
And never, no, never
No more would her Granny
Set eyes upon Annie.
So as the dusk grew

More deep, and the dew
More silvery sweet,
And as the pale fleet
Of shimmery moth
Came floating like froth
Of the moon, little Ann
Followed Grandmother's plan
And stayed by the hearth.
But she thought of the path
Through sweet-scented dew-sodden
Thyme and Old Man,
Which mustn't be trodden
'Twixt seven and seven
On Midsummer Even
By wondering Ann.

## THE WIND HAS TAKEN THE DAMSON TREE

The wind has taken the damson tree,
He was as old as old could be;
A wrinkled graybeard with crooked spine,
He held up Alice's washing-line.

His neck was curved like a twisted S,
Crowned in May with loveliness,
A pow of snow hung high in air,
Unsupported it looked up there.

Afar on the road you saw it sway
Shining against the pale blue day;
The fairest thing, oh the fairest thing,
Was the old damson's head in spring.

Nodding above the playful jests
Of the wind among the silky vests,
The full-blown skirts, and the lively legs
Of stockings, pinned by their wooden pegs.

His old boughs chuckled, his blossoms smiled,
Whenever the wind of spring grew wild,
And primrose petticoat, violet gown,
And lily overall tumbled down.

Tall and thin in the kitchen plot
He stood and pondered, when June was hot
And his flower was done and his fruit to come,
Stood and pondered his sweet blue plum.

August came, the paddock was mowed,
The first corn fell, and he dropped his load;
He heard rich praise of his pies, and then,
"The old 'un's done it," he thought, "again!"

But come October a bullying gale
Blew and blustered. And age is frail.
Where the petticoats fell, falls he.
The wind has taken the damson tree.


## FOR CHRISTMAS DAY

A carol round the ruddy hearth,
   A song outside the door—
Let Christmas Day make sure its lay
   Sounds sweetly to the poor.

A turkey in the baking-tin,
   A pudding in the pot—
Let Christmas Day the hunger stay
   In them that have not got.

Red berries on the picture-frame,
   White berries in the hall—
Let Christmas Day look twice as gay
   With evergreens for all.

A stocking on the chimneypiece,
  A present on the chair—
Let Christmas Day not pass away
  Till those who have do share.

A star upon the midnight sky,
  A shepherd looking East—
On Christmas Day let all men pray,
  And not till after, feast.


## CAROL OF THE SIGNS

Whiter than silver shines
Last night's fallen snow,
It is thick with signs,
Yet I saw none go.

Naked feet, three pair,
Left prints upon the snow,
Because the feet were bare,
Poor men's feet, I know.

Wheels of chariots rolled
Last night across the snow,
Great men in the cold
Rode before cockcrow.

Lo! a newborn lamb
Ran on the fallen snow,
By his side his dam
Gently trod and slow.

Here a Cross was laid
Heavy on the snow,
Somebody here stayed
To rest a moment so.

And here, the brightest scar
Of all upon the snow,
The imprint of a Star,
A heavenly Star, dropped low.

Thick as dew on grass
Lie signs upon the snow,
Yet I heard none pass,
And I saw none go.

## THIS HOLY NIGHT

God bless your house this holy night,
    And all within it;

God bless the candle that you light
    To midnight's minute:

The board at which you break your bread,
    The cup you drink of:

And as you raise it, the unsaid
    Name that you think of:

The warming fire, the bed of rest,
    The ringing laughter:

These things, and all things else be blest
    From floor to rafter

This holy night, from dark to light,
    Even more than other

And, if you have no house to-night,
    God bless you, brother.

## THE RIDING OF THE KINGS

In a far land upon a day,
Where never snow did fall,
Three Kings went riding on the way
Bearing presents all.

And one wore red, and one wore gold,
And one was clad in green,
And one was young, and one was old,
And one was in between.

The middle one had human sense,
The young had loving eyes,
The old had much experience,
And all of them were wise.

Choosing no guide by eve and morn
But heaven's starry drifts,
They rode to find the Newly-Born
For whom they carried gifts.

Oh, far away in time they rode
Upon their wanderings,
And still in story goes abroad
The riding of the Kings.

So wise, that in their chosen hour,
As through the world they filed,
They sought not wealth or place or power,
But rode to find a Child.

## BETHLEM BELLS

On Christmas Eve in Palestine
They'll ring the Bells of Bethlehem,
In Palestine, in Palestine,
    Bethlem Bells will ring!
Listen, listen, listen, listen,
Listen in to Palestine!
      Fine and thin
      The silver din
    In every ear shall sing!

On Christmas Eve in Palestine
They rang no bell in Bethlehem,
Long ago in Palestine
    Bethlem Bells were dumb.
Yet the heavenly choristers
Were singing over Palestine
      Long and strong
      Their golden song
Of the King to come.

On Christmas Eve in Palestine,
Hark! the Bells of Bethlehem!
In Palestine, in Palestine,
    Bethlem Bells do ring!
      Silver din
      And golden song,
      Fine and thin,
      Long and strong—
Listen, listen, listen, listen!
*Gloria! Gloria! Gloria!*
All the Bells of Bethlehem
Are ringing in the King!

## THE MOTHER'S TALE

Just before bed,
"Oh, *one* more story,
Mother!" they said;
And in the glory
Of red and gold
Beyond the fender
Their Mother told
Splendor on splendor.

A small boy threw
A handful of seeds,
And a beanstalk grew
Faster than weeds
As high as heaven . . .
She wore a red hood . . .
Once there were seven
Dwarfs in a wood . . .

So the children found
A gingerbread house . . .
So Puss with a bound
Killed the Giant-mouse . . .
"Now, Mother, tell a
*Best* tale of all!"
So Cinderella
Went to the ball . . .

"Don't stop, Mother!"
It's time to rest.
"Oh, tell us another,
The *very* best!"
So the best of all
She told to them:
"Once in a stall
In Bethlehem . . ."

## THE MOTHER'S SONG

She knew, the Maiden Mother knew,
Singing in the stable dim,
She sang for all the children who
Ever should come after Him;
Holding Him on either hand,
She knew they were not one and one,
But she was every mother and
He was every mother's son.

"Thou little thing, thou little thing!
All the joy of earth is thine.
More men's eyes shall shine for thee
Than stars shall in the heavens shine.

"Thou little thing, thou little thing!
To all sorrow art thou wed.
Men shall shed more tears for thee
Than heaven drops of rain shall shed.

"Thou little thing, thou little thing!
All things born thy name shall know.
More small tongues shall utter thee
Than daisies shall in meadows grow.

"Thou little thing, thou little thing!
All the world shall follow thee.
More souls shalt thou to heaven bring
Than birds shall fly from sea to sea.

"Thou little thing, thou little thing!
Each death is thine, and every birth.
Thou shalt more often live and die
Than all the peoples of the earth."

She knew, the Maiden Mother knew,
When she sang her child to sleep,
She sang for all the mothers who
Ever had a child in keep.
Lulling him upon her breast,
She knew, as she that burden bore,
She all children sang to rest
With her own for evermore.

## THE CHILD AND THE BIRD

The Child:  My Bird, why do you sing no more?
I used to think I never heard
A voice so sweet as yours before.
Why do you sing no more, my Bird?

The Bird:  Ah, could you sing, or would you try,
If you had wings, and could not fly?

The Child:  But look, my Bird! I've given you
A little cottage for your own,
With wicker bars I painted blue,
The prettiest cottage ever known.

The Bird:  Oh, once I had the two blue domes
Of night and morning for my homes.

The Child:  But every day I bring you seeds,
And water in a little pan,
I hunt the garden for green weeds
To give you pleasure when I can.

The Bird:  But once the whole earth was the wild
Green garden that I fed in, Child.

The Child:  But look! no storm can hurt you now,
I shield you from the hail and rain,
Safer you are than on the bough,
So sing again, oh sing again!

The Bird:    Ah, safety gives me no such powers
           To sing, as joy does after showers.

The Child:    My Bird, I cannot let you go!
           Your feathers are so soft and fine!
           I love you so, I want you so,
           I must, I *must* have you for mine!

The Bird:    Yours in a cage I cannot be.
           I was your own when I was free.

           Open the doors! and you shall hear
           Such singing as you never heard.
           Open the doors! and then, my dear,
           All birds shall be your singing-bird,
           A thousand birds instead of one,
           Singing and singing in the sun.

           The crooning dove, the happy thrush,
           The skylark trilling on the edge
           Of light, the warblers in the rush,
           The cheeping pipers in the hedge,
           All these shall be for ever yours
           The moment you undo my doors.

The Child:    My Bird, I do not understand.
           I thought if I could only catch
           You fast inside my very hand
           You must be mine. But there's the latch
           Undone. Now fly away and sing,
           Oh sing again, you pretty thing.

The Bird:    Sweet! in your garden wrens shall nest,
           And swallows build below your eaves.
           Sweet! on your sill shall robins rest,
           And blackbirds whistle from your leaves.
           And every year, when songs are new,
           Sweet! they shall all belong to you.

# Over the Garden Wall

# OVER THE GARDEN WALL

Over the garden wall,
Where unseen children play,
Somebody threw a ball
One fine summer day.
I caught it as it came
Straight from the hand unknown
Playing a happy game
It would not play alone.

A pretty ball with bands
Of gold and stars of blue;
I turned it in my hands
And wondered, then I threw
Over the garden wall
Again the treasure round—
And somebody caught the ball
With a laughing sound.

# THE SOUNDS IN THE MORNING

The sounds in the morning
Go all down the street:
The tapping of sticks
And the patter of feet,
The wind in the plane-trees
That whisper and rustle,
The pigeons all sleepy,
The newsboys all hustle,
The *clippety-clop*
And the *clip-clop* again
Of soldiers and horses,

More horses than men,
The clatter of milk-cans,
The chatter of maids,
The slop of their buckets,
The sort without spades,
And sometimes the mooing
Of slow-moving cows
Brings the smell of the lowlands
To me as I drowse,
And sometimes the bleating
And scuffle of sheep
Draws down the high hill-tops
To me half-asleep,
Dogs barking, bells chiming,
The twitter of sparrows—
Till the sun through the slats
Of my blind shoots his arrows,
And the world of my ears
Seems to dwindle in size
As I jump out of bed
To the world of my eyes.

## GETTING OUT OF BED

Up with you, lazybones!
Over the brink!
Don't stop to pick up heart,
Don't stop to think,

Don't stop for *any*thing!
Jump out of bed,
Gather your garments
Wherever they're shed.

The chair has your stocking,
The table your vest,
Your shoe's in the fender,
Your shirt's on the chest,

Your belt's on the door-knob,
And you are in bed;
Wake yourself, shake yourself,
Up, sleepy head!


## GOOD MORNING

Good morning, nurse, good morning, cook,
Good morning, all of you;
Good morning to my picture-book,
And to my window-view.

Good morning to the bird out there
That cannot sing enough,
And to the carpet which my bare
Feet press on, soft and rough.

Good morning to the breakfast smell
That rises from below,
And to the breakfast sound as well
That clatters to and fro.

Good morning, Towzer! Come, let's run,
Jump, shout, and laugh and sing—
Good morning to you, every one!
Good morning, everything!

## BREAKFAST

Is it coffee for breakfast?
I wish it was tea!
Is it jam? Oh, why can't there
Be honey for me?

Is it brown bread-and-butter?
I wish it was toast!
Is it just bread-and-milk?
I like porridge the most.

Is it soft-boiled eggs? Brother!
I'd rather have fried.
You *know* I don't like soft-boiled eggs,
Though I've tried.

Of all horrid breakfasts
This breakfast's the worst!—
*Who tumbled out of his bed*
*Wrong leg first?*


## THERE ISN'T TIME!

There isn't time, there isn't time
To do the things I want to do,
With all the mountain-tops to climb,
And all the woods to wander through,
And all the seas to sail upon,
And everywhere there is to go,
And all the people, every one
Who lives upon the earth, to know.
There's only time, there's only time
To know a few, and do a few,
And then sit down and make a rhyme
About the rest I want to do.

## CHILD AND DOG

Hello, Towzer! what's he after?
  Cocking head all on one side,
Grinning mouth that pleads with laughter—
  *Master!*—not to be denied.

Lolling tongue and tail a-wagging,
  So persuasive—*master, please!*—
One ear cocked and t'other flagging,
  There is no resisting these!

Quick small feet on legs a-straddle,
  Eyes with loving hopes abrim—
Master! do you *think* some lad'll
  Throw his ball and play with him?

## LESSONS

William the Conqueror, Ten-Sixtysix—
I know what I'll build after tea with my bricks!
I'll build a great castle with drawbridge and keep,
And arches through which I shall see, when I peep,
Saxon and Norman both up to their tricks. . . .
William the Conqueror, Ten-Sixtysix.

Madrid is the Capital City of Spain—
I know what I'll do if it only won't rain!
I'll set my new boat in full sail on the lake,
Commanded by Hawkins and Raleigh and Drake,
To conquer the Spanish Armada again . . .
Madrid is the Capital City of Spain.

## A KITTEN

He's nothing much but fur
And two round eyes of blue,
He has a giant purr
And a midget mew.

He darts and pats the air,
He starts and cocks his ear,
When there is nothing there
For him to see and hear.

He runs around in rings,
But why we cannot tell;
With sideways leaps he springs
At things invisible—

Then half-way through a leap
His startled eyeballs close,
And he drops off to sleep
With one paw on his nose.

## THE GOLDEN CAT

My golden cat has dappled sides;
No prince has worn so fine a cloak,
Patterned like sea-water where rides
The sun, or like the flower in oak
When the rough plank has been planed out,
Lovely as yellow mackerel skies
In moonlight, or a speckled trout.
Clear as swung honey were his eyes.

It was a wondrous daily thing
To look for, when his beautiful
Curved body gathered for a spring
That, light as any golden gull,
Flashed over the fine net of wire
Which my casement-window bars;
His leap was bright as tongues of fire,
And swift as autumn shooting-stars.

My cat was like a golden gift,
A golden myth of Grecian lore—
But things so bright, and things so swift,
Must vanish; and he is no more.

## THE QUARREL

I quarreled with my brother,
I don't know what about,
One thing led to another
And somehow we fell out.
The start of it was slight,
The end of it was strong,
He said he was right,
I knew he was wrong!

We hated one another.
The afternoon turned black.
Then suddenly my brother
Thumped me on the back,
And said, "Oh, *come* along!
We can't go on all night—
*I* was in the wrong."
So he was in the right.

## MARY INDOORS

Aren't you coming out, Mary?
    Come out: your eyes will tire—
Oh, let me be, please, please, said she,
    I want to read by the fire.

What are you reading, Mary,
    That keeps you, keeps you in?—
Oh, wonderful things of knights and kings,
    With their heart's desire to win.

Look out of window, Mary!
    The blustering day is bright.
Come fight the wind with us, and find
    The sun on the hilly height.

Come on out of it, Mary,
    And win your heart's desire!—
Oh, let me be, please, *please,* said she,
    I want to read by the fire.


## BOREDOM

Oh dear! what shall I do?
Nothing lasts more than a minute or two,
Everything's silly, and nothing is fun,
And there doesn't seem anything left to be done.

Oh, dear! what shall I do?
I've read all my fairy-tales seven times through,
I'm tired of my bricks and I'm sick of my train,
And my paint-box was left out all night in the rain.

Oh dear! what shall I do?
I don't *want* to go in the garden with you,
I don't *want* to sit down and play a nice game,
I want to do something that isn't the same.

Everything, everything *is* such a bore!
I don't enjoy being alive any more.
Why can't there sometimes be something that's new?
Oh dear! *what shall I* DO?

## SOME ONE TO TEA

Somebody's coming to tea to-day.
   Oh, what a treat for you and me!
Perhaps my Mother will let us play
   With the musical box when we've done tea;

Perhaps, perhaps she is going to make
   Buttery scones for you and me,
Perhaps, perhaps there'll be chocolate cake,
   And pineapple jam, not raspberry.

Somebody's coming to tea to-day!
   There might be crackers for you and me!
Perhaps my Father will come and say
   We're going to have fireworks, after tea.

Perhaps he'll need somebody near to hold
   The Bengal Lights, and it might be me
Who waves the streamer of green or gold,
   And you the scarlet one after tea.

Somebody's coming to tea to-day.
   What will it mean to you and me?
It all depends, in a sort of way,
   On whether he's seven or fifty-three.

## AFTER TEA

Listen! that's Mother singing and playing.
    Oh, what a lovely chance!
The lights are down and the shadows are swaying,
    Let us go sing and dance.

She'll smile at us, but she won't stop singing.
    The sweetest tunes she knows.
In the far corners the shadows are swinging,
    The fire on the ceiling glows.

Nobody plays such music as Mother.
    She plays it for me and you.
The shadows are dancing with one another—
    Let us start dancing too.

## BEDTIME

Five minutes, five minutes more, please!
    Let me stay five minutes more!
Can't I just finish the castle
    I'm building here on the floor?
Can't I just finish the story
    I'm reading here in my book?
Can't I just finish this bead-chain—
    It *almost* is finished, look!
Can't I just finish this game, please?
    When a game's once begun
It's a pity never to find out
    Whether you've lost or won.
Can't I just stay five minutes?
    Well, can't I stay just four?
Three minutes, then? two minutes?
    Can't I stay *one* minute more?

## ON THE STAIRCASE

The stair-carpet is Turkey red,
  The bannister is brown—
If only going up-stairs
  Were as quick as coming down!

It's easy before breakfast-time,
  Never thinking twice,
To slide down on the bannister
  And be there in a trice.

But oh, it's hard at bedtime
  To climb the carpet-stair,
Leaving far behind you
  The world and all that's there!

Brown is the bannister,
  The carpet Turkey red—
It's horrid on the staircase
  Going up to bed.


## GOING TO BED

Oh dear! *need* I brush my hair?
*Need* I get the tangles clear?
If it's tangled, *I* don't care!
*Need* I do my teeth? O dear!

*Need* I wash right up my arm?
*Need* I wash my other ear?
If it's dirty, where's the harm?
*Need* I wash my neck? Oh dear!

Need I untie *every* knot?
*Need* I fold my clothes just here?
*Can't* I simply on the spot
Tumble into bed? Oh dear!

## THE SOUNDS IN THE EVENING

The sounds in the evening
Go all through the house,
The click of the clock
And the pick of the mouse,
The footsteps of people
Upon the top floor,
The skirts of my mother
That brush by my door,
The crick in the boards,
And the creak of the chairs,
The fluttering murmurs
Outside on the stairs,
The ring at the bell,
The arrival of guests,
The laugh of my father
At one of his jests,
The clashing of dishes
As dinner goes in,
The babble of voices
That distance makes thin,
The mewings of cats
That seem just by my ear,
The hooting of owls
That can never seem near,
The queer little noises
That no one explains—
Till the moon through the slats
Of my window-blind rains,

And the world of my eyes
And my ears melts like steam
As I find in my pillow
The world of my dream.


## A DRINK OF WATER

Mother has gone away. The night is black
Whatever can I do to bring her back?
She tucked me in and kissed me' once for all
And said good night, and told me not to call,
But oh, I want her so, I want her so!
What can I do to make her come? I know —
Mother! Mother! *Mo*-ther! (Listen! she's
Coming!) I want a drink of water, please.

Will she, when she comes to me, be vexed?
I don't care! I'll see her standing next
My bed, and hear her voice and touch her dress.
Will she, when she comes, I wonder, guess
I'm not *really* thirsty? *I* don't care!
I'll see her face again and smell her hair
As I sit in bed upon my knees—
Mother! I want a drink of water, please.

She's come and gone. She held against my lips
The bedroom glass. I drank it in small sips
To make it last. She said, "Don't call again,
Darling," and smoothed the sheet and counterpane,
Kissed me, and went downstairs again. But oh,
I want her so, I want to see her so!
Mother! Mother! *Mo*-ther! *Mother!* (She's
Coming!) Another drink of water, please.

## IN BED

The fire upon my ceiling glows
At bedtime like a restless rose;
Long after lights are out it wakes
The corners of the room, and makes
So many a delicious leap
I find it hard to go to sleep.

The flames are naughty little boys
Who making hardly any noise
Dance through the room, just as my thought
Does in my head, and can't be caught,
And only under cover creep
When the coal has gone to sleep.

Then where the ruddy fire-boys leapt
The room grows very dark, except
Upon the ceiling one bright square
From the lamp that stands out there
All night to drive away the deep
Shadows from us while we sleep.

## WAKING AT NIGHT

What has happened? Is this me?
Who am I? Where can I be?
Where's the fireplace? Where's the door?
I can't remember any more.

If I'm me, the rocking-chair
*Should* be in the window there,
But the window's turned around
In the dark, and can't be found.

Strange that though the room is dark
I just know it's twisted. Hark!
That's the cuckoo-clock—how queer!—
Ticking there instead of here.

Something's happened to my bed,
Head is foot and foot is head,
And the wall has shifted quite
From my left side to my right.

Then this room is *not* the one
I know—it has come undone,
Window, fireplace, door and wall,
And I can't be me at all!

## GOING INTO DREAM

Where are you going, child, so far away?
Where you cannot follow to watch me at my play,
Light as a fallen feather floating on the stream
I'm going, going, back into the dream.

What will you find there, child, what will you do?
Something that I cannot ever tell to you,
Quiet as a moth flies across the candle-beam
I'm going, going back into the dream.

## THE LIGHTS AT NIGHT

No sooner does the sky grow dark
Than all the town breaks out in lights,
Blue and green and crimson spark
Making a thousand startling sights.

The theaters and advertisements
Dazzle the night with brilliant signs,
And high in air the world's events
Are writ in running golden lines.

The fiery pictures glow and fade,
Clusters of stars wink in and out,
The flood-lights pour their bright cascade
From domes and towers round about.

It is as though a magic spell
Had brought to life a fairy town—
Oh, what a jeweled citadel
Is London when the dark comes down!


SNOWFALL

Oh, that first dazzled window-glance!
Oh, that first fall of freshest snow!
Is it a new world come by chance,
Or still the old world children know?

Where is the grass, and where's the road?
How everything is changed out there!
The bush is molded by its load,
The tree is carved upon the air.

It is as though the house last night
Moved through the darkness, traveling
Into a magic morn of white
While nobody felt anything:

A morn all clear and crisp that rose
Upon a land all strange and still,

A morn where ice and silence froze
The land into a trance, until

A boy with a delighted shout
The crystal of that trance should break,
And, to its promise rushing out,
Startle all the snow awake.


## WHAT I'VE BEEN DOING

What have I been doing, then,
To get myself in such a state?
I only stood and watched the men,
Painting Mrs. Loveday's gate,

I only went down to the brook
To catch a minnow for my jar,
I only went along to look
At Mr. Warren's motor-car,

I only climbed the walnut-tree
And slithered down along the trunk,
And reached inside the butt to see
If I could find my hat, which sunk,

I only went into the sty
To help to give the pigs their swill,
I only thought I'd like to try
To carry home a whole mole-hill,

Whatever can I have been at?
What have I been doing, then?
Nothing much—and nothing that
I shan't often do again.

## SOLDIERS AND HORSES

### *(Early Morning)*

Down the hilly avenue,
Autumn in the air,
Young soldiers riding
A double line of horses,
One horse ridden,
And one horse bare.

An eager boy beside them
Kept a level race;
Forty pair of horses
With their easy riders,
For half-a-mile downhill
Went at walking-pace.

Half-a-mile of moving
Dark and golden flanks,
Supple pasterns curving,
Strong legs and slender
Never stopping moving
In their double ranks.

Young men upright,
Looking straight ahead,
Turning in their saddles,
Laughing to a comrade,
Masters of their horses,
The laden and the led.

## THE MILK-CART PONY

The milk-cart pony in the street
   Is spotted white and brown,
He frisks his mane, he kicks his feet,
   And rattles through the town.

His milk-cans glitter in the sun,
   His harness clinks and rings,
The milk-cart pony on the run
   Must think of lively things.

Perhaps he thinks of circus-tents
   And ladies in top hats,
And orange-peel and sawdust scents,
   And clowns and acrobats.

Perhaps he thinks of Derby Day
   With crowds upon the course
All shouting loud *Hip hip hooray!*
   *Here comes the winning horse!*

Perhaps he thinks of Dartymoor
   Where he was once a child,
And on the purple-heather floor
   The ponies still run wild.

Well, nobody knows *what* he thinks,
   This little skewbald clown,
Who bears our night and morning drinks
   So noisily through town!

## JIM AT THE CORNER

Jim was a Sailor
Who sailed on the sea.
Now he sits at the corner
From breakfast to tea,
With a nod and a twinkle
For you and for me.

His hair is quite silver,
His eyes are quite blue,
His legs have got pains
So he's nothing to do
But to nod and to twinkle
At me and at you.

He tells all the weather
Without any fuss,
When he says it is thus
Then of *course* it is thus;
He nods as he says it
And twinkles at us.

He knows the world over
From east to west rim,
Now he sits on his box
And the whole world knows **Jim.**
He nods to the world,
And the world nods to him.

## THE CITY SHOW

"Here sits the Lord Mayor,
  Here sit his two men"—
Drawn in gold coaches
  Through London again.

Big people, small people,
  Look where you will,
Crowd on the curbstone
  And hang on the sill,

To see the old story
  Of London unrolled
Through the ways of the City
  In scarlet and gold.

Clear off the traffic there!
  Empty the street!
Scatter the sand that will
  Make the road sweet!

Hark to the trumpeters!
  Listen, the drums!
Look, Dicky, quick, Dicky,
  See, here it comes!

Here's the procession
  That ends in Guildhall,
Shopkeepers, Aldermen,
  Lord Mayor and all.

And Dicky, with holes
  In his stocking and crown,
Thinks, "I might be Lord Mayor
  One day of the Town!"

## THE BOY

Is it, I wonder, a rum thing,
  Or nothing to wonder upon,
That whenever a man's doing something
  There's always a boy looking on?

If he's mending a road or a motor,
  If he's loading a crane or a van,
If he's tinkering at an old boat or
  A boot, there's a boy near the man.

If he's climbing a tree or a steeple,
  Or shoeing a horse to the joy
Of a number of on-looking people,
  You'll find at his elbow a boy.

If he's wrecking a house, if he's rubbing
  A window or building a wall,
Unmoving, unmoved, and past snubbing,
  There's a boy in the forefront of all.

If he's doing odd things with the drainpipes,
  If he's pouring hot tar on the street,
Or playing about with the main pipes,
  There's a boy almost under his feet.

He may stand for hours like a dumb thing,
  But this can be counted upon—
Wherever a man's doing something
  There's always a boy looking on.

## HOUSE COMING DOWN

They're pulling down the house
    At the corner of the Square,
The floors and the ceilings
    Are out in the air,
The fireplaces so rusty,
The staircases so dusty,
And wallpaper so musty,
    Are all laid bare.

It looks like a doll's house
    With the dolls put away,
And the furniture laid by
    Against another day;
No bed to lie in,
No pan to fry in,
Or dish to make a pie in,
    And nobody to play.

That was the parlor
    With the cream-and-yellow scrawls,
That was the bedroom
    With the roses on the walls,
There's a dark red lining
In the room they had for dining,
And a brown one, rather shining,
    Goes all up the halls.

But where is the lady
    In a pretty gown?
Where is the baby
    That used to crow and frown?
Oh, the rooms look so little,
The house looks so brittle,
And no one cares a tittle
    If it all tumbles down.

## WINDOW-BOXES

A window-box of pansies
Is such a happy thing,
A window-box of wallflowers
Is a garden for a king,
A window-box of roses
Makes every one stand still
Who sees a garden growing
On a window-sill.

## THE STREET FOUNTAIN

They've put a fountain in the road
In memory of Samuel Jones.
Now every horse that draws a load
Beside the trough can stay his bones,

And stoop to lap the water up,
And every man can dip his lips
Into the ice-cold metal cup
Under the spout that always drips.

I don't know why a fountain runs
For Samuel Jones. I don't know who
He was. Perhaps the desert suns
Once made him pray to God for dew;

Perhaps a silent vow he took
That if he came again to know
An English river, pond, or brook,
He'd make another fountain flow—

That many a man with throat gone dry,
And thirsty horse, should bless again
The day beneath a burning sky
When God sent Samuel Jones the rain.


## THE TRUE TALE OF
## GRANDFATHER PENNY

Grandfather Penny
Of Euston is dead.
Untended of any
He died in his bed.
He died without mother
Or sister or brother
It's whispered by many
He died without bread.

But the children that knew him,
Who play in the streets,
Would always run to him
To get penny treats.
When bread puts its price on,
He never thought twice on
The gift of a penny
For poor children's sweets.

Grandfather Penny,
Old, gentle, and thin,
There will not be many
To heaven who win,
Whose penny rings sweeter
In ear of Saint Peter,
When he opens the gate
And says, "Granfer, come in."

## AIR-BALLOONS

There's the man who sells balloons!
With golden suns and white full moons,
Pale green grapes and purple plums
On his shoulder, here he comes!
Just above his hat's old brim
Silver airships shine and swim.

Which to-day shall be the one?
White full moon or golden sun,
Purple plum or pale green grape,
Or will you have the other shape,
That beautiful bright oval there,
The silver ship that floats in air?

Take care not to prick it, though:
Moon and sun that bump and blow
Shrivel at the prick of pins,
And grape and plum are withered skins,
And airships crumple up like dry
Leaves, never, never more to fly.

## MRS. PECK-PIGEON

Mrs. Peck-Pigeon
Is picking for bread,
Bob-bob-bob
Goes her little round head.
Tame as a pussy-cat
In the street,
Step-step-step
Go her little red feet.

With her little red feet
And her little round head,
Mrs. Peck-Pigeon
Goes picking for bread.


## LONDON SPARROW

Sparrow, you little brown gutter-mouse,
How can I tempt you into the house?
I scatter my crumbs on the window-sill
But down in the gutter you're hopping still:
I strew my cake at the open door,
But you don't seem to know what cake is for!
I drop my cherries where you can see,
I bring you water, I whistle *"Twee!"*—
But nothing I offer, and nothing I utter
Fetches the sparrow out of the gutter.
What is it makes the road so nice
For sparrows, the little brown gutter-mice?


## THE SMOKE

Over there
Is a little house,
Quiet as a mouse,
Or an empty hive,
Or as death.
But up in the air
From the chimney-poke
Goes the gentle smoke,
And I know that the house is alive,
I can see its breath.

## BLIND ALLEY

There's a turning I must pass
Often four times in a day,
Narrow, rather dark, with grass
Growing, a neglected way;

Two long walls, a tumbled shed,
Bushes shadowing each wall—
When I've wondered where it led
People say Nowhere at all.

But if that is true, oh why
Should this turning be at all?
Some time, in the daylight, I
*Will* creep up along the wall;

For it somehow makes you think,
It has such a secret air,
It might lead you to the brink
Of—oh well, of anywhere!

Some time I will go. And see,
Here's the turning just in sight,
Full of shadows beckoning me!
Some time, yes. But not to-night.

## FOOD OUT-OF-DOORS

Can't mutton be dull,
And potatoes be dull,
And pudding be dull,
  And slices of bread,

With four walls all round,
And a floor for the ground,
And a ceiling all sound
    And safe overhead?

And *can't* bread be sweet,
And slices of meat,
And pudding to eat,
    What beautiful fare
With trees all around,
And grass on the ground,
And the sky full of sound
    Of the birds in the air!

## SISTERS

"Come!" cried Helen, eager Helen.
*"Time enough,"* said careful Ann.
But oh, the lilac-buds were swelling
And all the birds had started telling—
"Listen! look!" cried eager Helen,
Pointing where the spring began.
*"Well, and what of that?"* said Ann.
"Something's happening—oh, let's go!"
*"When it happens we shall know."*
"Ah, but that's so slow!" cried Helen,
"Come on, come!" cried eager Helen.
        *"Time enough,"* said Ann.
"I must go!" *"And I will wait.
You'll be too soon."* "You'll be too late!"
*"Who knows?"* said Ann. "Come on!" cried Helen,
        And ran and ran and ran.

## JENNY WHITE AND JOHNNY BLACK

Jenny White and Johnny Black
Went out for a walk.
Jenny found wild strawberries,
And John a lump of chalk.

Jenny White and Johnny Black
Clambered up the hill.
Jenny heard a willow-wren
And John a workman's drill.

Jenny White and Johnny Black
Wandered by the dyke.
Jenny smelt the meadow-sweet,
And John a motor-bike.

Jenny White and Johnny Black
Turned into the lane.
Jenny saw the moon by day,
And Johnny saw a train.

Jenny White and Johnny Black
Walked into a storm.
Each felt for the other's hand
And found it nice and warm.

## THE BUTTERCUP FIELD

The buttercup field, oh the buttercup field,
Where the buttercups grow like trees
Over my running baby's head
And the standing cattle's knees.

The buttercup field, oh the buttercup field!
And isn't my baby bold
To run away from his mother's arms
Into a world of gold?

The buttercup field, oh the buttercup field
Where my baby found his way
Through a jungle of green and golden trees,
And all the way back one day.

## HIDDEN

In the green wood the doves all coo—
    But where are the doves? I cannot see them.
The leaves are thick, yet the light falls through—
    But where is the sun? I cannot see him.
There's a smell of violets in the dew—
    But where are the flowers? I cannot see them.
I know you are there, I am looking for you—
    Oh where, where are you? I cannot see you.

## KEEP STILL

Look, and keep very still,
Still as a tree,
And if you do you will
Presently see
The doe come down to drink
Leading her fawn
Just as they did, I think,
In the first dawn.

Hark, not a sound, my dear,
Be quiet and hark,
And very soon you'll hear
The vixen bark,
And see her cubs at play
As I believe
They played in starlight gray
On the first eve.

Look, and keep very still.
Hark, not a sound!
The pretty creatures will
Soon be around,
At play and drink, as though
They drank and played,
Cub, vixen, fawn and doe,
Ere men were made.

## IN GOES ROBIN

In goes Robin, bold as brass,
Into all that moving mass
Of blue and green and creamy foam
Just as though he were at home.
Water doesn't frighten him,
He will sink till he can swim,
When a big wave knocks him down
Up will come his laughing brown
Spluttering face. He has no fear,
The sea is his: yes, all that clear
Stretch of water, touching all
The shores of earth, that makes its call
On English cliffs and Indian sands,
And coral isles and mountain-lands,

And crowded ports and lonely bays:
His, when he choose to go those ways,
With all the ships that sail on it,

And all the gulls and mews that flit,
And all the fishes in the blue,
And all the wrecks and icebergs too.
The sea was Robin's from the first,
He saw it and was all athirst,
He couldn't *wait* to reach it—whether
Its waves were tumbled all together,
Or was it bright and smooth as glass,
In went Robin, bold as brass.


## THE VILLAGE GREEN

Upon the Village Green
A-many sights are seen:
The dancing of the little girls when May-Day crowns a
Queen,
The games that little boys
Play with so much noise,
The peddlers' booths on market-days that sell you cakes and
toys,
The gipsy caravan
Cluttered with pot and pan,
The fight 'twixt Butcher's Aberdeen and Blacksmith's Black-
and-Tan,
The organ-grinder rare
As nuts in May, though ne'er
A summer will go by us but some evening he is there.
And then the duck-pond, round
As a cartwheel on the ground,
Where podgy ducks and snowy geese are always to be found,

And horses stop to drink,
And children at the brink
Stoop down to launch their paper boats, and see them swim or
sink,
And aged folk at ease
Under the aspen trees
A-telling how the olden times were better times than these,
And some young country miss
Giving her lad a kiss,
Quite certain that the olden times were not so good as this.
And daisies small and sweet,
And stocks that used to meet,
But haven't met this many a day, above the vagrant's feet—
Sure, nothing that has been
Has not been done and seen
'Twixt one year's start and one year's end upon the Village
Green.

## JILL CAME FROM THE FAIR

Jill came from the Fair
With her pennies all spent.
She had had her full share
Of delight and content;
She had ridden the ring
To a wonderful tune,
She had flown in a swing
Half as high as the moon,
In a boat that was drawn
By an ivory swan
Beside a green lawn
On a lake she had gone,
She had bought a gold packet
That held her desire,

She had touched the red jacket
Of one who ate fire,
She had stood at the butt,
And although she was small
She had won a rough nut
With the throw of a ball,
And across the broad back
Of a donkey a-straddle,
She had jolted like Jack-
In-the-Box on a saddle—
Till mid frolic and shout
And tinsel and litter,
The lights started out
Making everything glitter,
And dazed by the noise
And the blare and the flare,
With her toys and her joys
Jill came from the Fair.


## SUE WENT TO THE FAIR

Sue went to the Fair
With sixpence to spend—
And when she got there
It had come to an end!
The stall that sold sweets
And the tent that sold toys
Were cleared of their treats
For small girls and boys!
The big switchback stand
Was a skeleton hill,
The round-about band
Had grown silent, and still
As pictures the wagons,

The boats, and queer breeds
Of emus and dragons
And gold-saddled steeds;
The cocoanut sticks
Without heads stood about,
Like tall candle-wicks
Whose lights were blown out;
The shooting-booth had
Not a single bright prize
For the skilful young lad
Who could hit the bulls' eyes:
The tall spiral tower
Had fallen asleep,
And sent down no shower
Of folk in a heap;
And the motionless herds
Of red and blue swings
Hung listless as birds
That are clipped in their wings.
Oh where was the glitter
The Fair should reveal?
The grass was a litter
Of paper and peel,
The tent-ropes were slackened,
The flares were unlit,
The fairway was blackened
With cinders and grit!
And the men with brown arms,
And the girls with black hair
Who had packed up the charms
And the toys of the Fair,
Had no smiles for Sue.
She had come as their friend,
But nobody knew
She had sixpence to spend.

## THE MOTHER SINGS

Rockaby, my baby,
Slumber if you can.
I wonder what you're going to be
When you're grown a man.

If you are a monarch
On a gold and silver throne,
With all the lands of East and West
For to call your own,
I know you'll be the greatest monarch
Ever was known.

If you are a poet
With the magic of the word,
A swan's quill to write with
And a voice like a bird,
I know you'll be the greatest poet
Ever was heard.

But whether you're a monarch
And make your bride a queen,
Or whether you're a poet
With men's hearts to glean,
I know you are the sweetest baby
Ever was seen.
Rockaby, my baby,
Slumber if you can.
I wonder what you're going to be
When you're grown a man.

## COMFORTING

Hush now, hush now,
I heard her say,
What frightened you so?
It is gone away.
Was it a shadow?
Was it a sound?
Hush, it is gone now
And can't be found.
There, it shan't hurt you,
My own dear,
Dry eyes and smile again,
I am here.
Look then, it isn't
Anywhere!
Hush, darling, hush now,
There, there, there.

## SPOILT CHILD

Oh you little nuisance!
Oh you little sweet!
I could slap your naughty hands!
I could eat your precious feet!

No, you mustn't have it
When Mother tells you so,
Baby can't *have* it,
No, *no*, NO!

What, baby, screaming,
A big girl like you?
Very well, you've *got* it,
Stop screaming, do!

There now, you've dropped it!
Mother *knew* you would.
*Why* are you so naughty?
*Why* can't you be good?

I could shake you till you laugh,
I could kiss you till you cry!
Why can't I manage you,
Why, *why*, WHY?

## WHY?

Fie, darling! why do you cry? why do you **cry?**
Is it because the day is so long, is that why?
Or because your canary has died,
Or because you have tried
To climb up the pear-tree, and can't,
Or because your best aunt
Got married to-day
And went off to the Land of Cathay?
Is it because the fine present,
Whose thought was so pleasant,
Your father this morning agreed to bring **back from**
     the city,
Isn't nearly as pretty,
Or nearly as sweet, or as big, or as bright, oh **dear**
     me,
As you knew it was going to be?
Is *that* why you cried?
Or has the whole world grown too wi**de,**
Or too narrow, or something? or what?
Or have you forgot
Why you started to cry,
And you do not know why—is that why?

## CATCH IT!

Catch sun! catch sun!
Her little hands stretch
To the gold web spun,
Eager to fetch
The gift of the air
So lightly thrown
To everyone,
For her very own.

Catch rain! catch rain!
Her little hands grasp
At the silver chain,
Eager to clasp
The gift of the cloud,
Down-thrown, down-thrown
Again and again,
For her very own.

Catch rain! catch sun!
Her little hands snatch,
And into them run
What she never can catch.

## CHOOSING

Which will you have, a ball or a cake?
A cake is so nice, yes, that's what I'll take.

Which will you have, a cake or a cat?
A cat is so soft, I think I'll take that.

Which will you have, a cat or a rose?
A rose is so sweet, I'll have that, I suppose.

Which will you have, a rose or a book?
A book full of pictures?—oh, do let me look!

Which will you have, a book or a ball?
Oh, a ball! No, a book! No, a——
                    There! have them all!


## CLOSE OF DAY

When cocks say Cockadoodledoo!
  The tree-top shakes,
  The river wakes,
And the daisy gets her eye of dew.

When the cuckoo says Cuckoo!
  The tree-top rustles,
  The river bustles,
The daisy's eye is wide to view.

When the wood-dove murmurs Croo!
  The tree-top shrinks,
  The river blinks,
The daisy hangs her head anew.

And when the brown owl calls Tu-whoo!
  The tree-top closes,
  The river dozes,
The daisy sleeps, and so must you.


## ELIZABETH CRIED

Elizabeth cried
Because I came.
I never tried
To play a game,

I ate my meat
And I looked away—
Till Elizabeth's feet
Ran up, to stay.

We played a game
All over the place,
She said my name,
And I washed her face,
I gave her a ride—
Till my time was spent,
And Elizabeth cried
Because I went.

## RIDING IN BELMARY

Shall we go ride in Belmary?
How will we go?
On a mare as black as ebony,
And one as white as snow.
You shall ride the white mare
And I will ride the black,
Until we find the Perfect Knight
With a Cross upon his back.

## BOYS' NAMES

What splendid names for boys there are!
There's Carol like a rolling car,
And Martin like a flying bird,
And Adam like the Lord's First Word,
And Raymond like the Harvest Moon,
And Peter like a piper's tune,
And Alan like the flowing on
Of water. And there's John, like John.

## GIRLS' NAMES

What lovely names for girls there are!
There's Stella like the Evening Star,
And Sylvia like a rustling tree,
And Lola like a melody,
And Flora like a flowery morn,
And Sheila like a field of corn,
And Melusina like the moan
Of water. And there's Joan, like Joan.

## TIPPETTY WITCHET

Tippetty Witchet
Lived by a wood
In a blue pinafore
And a green hood;
Her hut was of wattle,
Her bed was of wool,
Her fire was of fircones,
Her bath was a pool.

She plaited sweet rushes
For shoes for her feet,
She bound birchen besoms
To keep her floor neat,
She picked fallen acorns
To roast for her tea,
And one of her picking
She set for a tree.

Tippetty Witchet
Died so long ago
That no one remembers

She ever was so;
Her wattles are scattered,
Her bed's trod in mire,
Her pool wants for water,
Her hearth has no fire.

But rich with tall timber,
And dark with broad shade,
Are fifty green acres
Round Tippetty's glade;
And old bones get brushwood
That's better than food,
And young bones get acorns
In Tippetty's wood.

And what does it matter
If nobody knows
Who gave the old these things,
And gave the young those,
Who wore a blue pinafore
And a green poke,
And planted the acorn
That turned into oak?

## BETWEEN THE BARS

Between the gold bars of her cot
Baby can see such a lot.
She sees her dolly on the floor
And wants to play with it once more;
The never-fading roses she
Can upon the carpet see,
And wants to pick them; in the grate,
Where she warmed her toes of late,

She sees the little dancing flames
And wants to join their flickering games.
Then she sees her Mother's face
Pressed all laughing in the space
Beside her pillow, with sweet lips
Seeking for her finger-tips
And the very last good-night
Kiss before she blows the light.
And then between the golden bars
She sees the coming of the stars
And the big round moon she knows,
And wants to go to them. And goes.


## OLD WIFE'S SONG

Once in a lifetime the white fawn run
'Twixt the falling of the moon and the rising of the sun.
If you can trap one he'll grant you your boon
'Twixt the falling of the sun and the rising of the moon.

Once in a lifetime the white falcon fly
'Twixt the clouding of the earth and the firing of the sky.
If you can snare one he'll give you your desire
'Twixt the waning of the cloud and the waxing of the fire.

You may ask what lies nearest to your heart and your mind,
From the kingdoms of the stars to the deserts of the wind,
Of the tongues of the birds the master shall you be,
And the wisdom of the roots, and the secrets of the sea.

But if you should fetter the fawn for good and all,
If with hood and jesses you keep the falcon thrall,
The wish you made for wisdom, for beauty, or for power,
Shall be to you a curse till your very last hour.

## WHITE HORSES

*Count the white horses you meet on the way,*
*Count the white horses, child, day after day,*
*Keep a wish ready for wishing—if you*
*Wish on the ninth horse, your wish will come true.*

I saw a white horse at the end of the lane,
I saw a white horse canter down by the shore,
I saw a white horse that was drawing a wain,
And one drinking out of a trough: that made four.

I saw a white horse gallop over the down,
I saw a white horse looking over a gate,
I saw a white horse on the way into town,
And one on the way coming back: that made eight.

But oh for the ninth one: where *he* tossed his mane,
And cantered and galloped and whinnied and swished
His silky white tail, I went looking in vain,
And the wish I had ready could never be wished.

*Count the white horses you meet on the way,*
*Count the white horses, child, day after day,*
*Keep a wish ready for wishing—if you*
*Wish on the ninth horse, your wish will come true.*


## THE BONNY BRIDE OF KENT

Bonny Bride, bonny Bride, mind how you tread!
What will you walk on, the day you are wed?

Wed with a cobbler and walk upon leather
(Dryfoot you'll go in the wettest of weather.)

Wed with a Joiner and walk upon wood
(The floors of your dwelling will always be good).

Wed with a Blacksmith and walk upon metal
(There'll never be leakage in saucepan or kettle).

Wed with a Baker and walk upon flour
(Bread shall not fail you until your last hour).

Wed with a Grocer and walk upon spice
(The pot in your kitchen shall always smell nice).

Wed with a Tailor and walk upon cloth
(Your clothes shall wear well against time and the
    moth).

Wed with a Gardener and walk upon roses
(All of your days shall be sweet as spring posies).

Bonny Bride, bonny Bride, look where you tread!
Mind what you walk on, the day you are wed!


## THE TALKING OF THE TREES

The Queen of Winter walks the land,
    Among the naked leas;
She hears, but does not understand,
    The talking of the trees.

"Oh the green days," they say, "the warm
    Green days of our content!"
The Birch-tree says, "I'll clothe my form
    In Spring with merriment."

The Poplar says, "I'll raise a tower
    Of leaves against the sky."

The Cherry says, "I'll shed my flower
    Ere four more moons go by."

The Oak-tree says, "Young nightingales
    Shall sing in me come May."
The Aspen says, "I'll shake my scales
    In June like silver spray."

The Elm-tree says, "I'll throw a sheaf
    Of shadow on the wheat."
The Beech-tree says, "I'll spread my leaf
    For coolness in the heat."

The Apple says, "Along my boughs
    I'll hang a hundred suns."
The Chestnut says, "Within my house
    Shall kneel a hundred nuns."

The Lime-tree says, "I'll draw a swarm
    Of bees upon my scent."
"Oh the green day," they say, "the warm
    Green day of our content!"

The Queen of Winter walks the land
    Among the naked leas.
She hears, but does not understand,
    The talking of the trees.

## THE SONG OF THE FIR

    There was a fir
    Within a wood,
    Far away, far away:
It stands no longer where it stood.
Dance around the tree today.

It had a scent
Made sweet the air,
Far away, far away:
The sweetness is no longer there.
Breathe the sweetness as you play,
And dance around the tree today.

It grew between
The earth and sky,
Far away, far away:
The tree has lost its liberty
And between four walls must stay.
Breathe the sweetness as you play,
And dance around the tree today.

On its tip
It bore a cone,
Far away, far away:
Now that simple fruit is gone
Hang the tree with presents gay
Mid the walls where it must stay,
Shedding sweetness where you play,
And dance around the tree today.


## THE TWO SWEETHEARTS

If you will come and be my queen
You'll have a gown of gold and green.

If you will come and be my wife
You'll go in cotton all your life.

If you will come and be my queen
Like peacocks you shall strut and preen.

If you will come and be my wife
You will do housework all your life.

If you will come and be my queen
You'll sleep behind a golden screen.

If you will come and be my wife
You'll sleep on stubble all your life.

If you will come and be my queen
I'll kiss your hand, by all men seen.

If you will come and be my wife
We'll kiss in secret all our life.


## LONG-GREEN-HILL

As I was going up Long-Green-Hill
I met a Long Green Lad.
Good-day, said I! Good-day, said he!
And no more words we had.

As I was going down Long-Green-Hill
I met a Low Gray Man.
Good-night, quoth I! Good-night, quoth he!
And we stopped where we began.


## JOSEPH FELL A-DREAMING

Joseph fell a-dreaming.
He dreamed of sheaves of grain;
One stood upright like a tree,
The rest bowed down again.

His dreams came with the night
And he told them in the noon.
He dreamed of the eleven stars,
The sun and the moon.

The sun was his father,
The moon was his mother,
Of all the stars, the brightest star
Was Benjamin his brother.

## MOON-COME-OUT

Moon-Come-Out
And Sun-Go-In,
Here's a soft blanket
To cuddle your chin.

Moon-Go-In
And Sun-Come-Out,
Throw off the blanket
And bustle about.

## THE GATE IN THE WALL

The blue gate in the wall,
The small blue gate is gone,
And I alone
Know all
That was once seen beyond this thick
Barrier of new brick.

There was a paved walk, long
And narrow,

Where the small throng
Of saxifrages green
Crept in between
The cracks; there was a barrow
Half full of withered flowers;
A pear tree, and a bush of silver broom;
And in that open room,
When there were sunny hours,
A graceful lady walked,
With hair as snowy as the pear-tree bloom,
And voice that always talked
As from a little distance. She
Was gone before the blue gate went from me.

But I shall see
Often through this new brick
What other eyes will not be quick
Enough to see:
The lady who once moved
Tending the beds and borders that she loved,
Whose work was never done,
Now in the early morning, now the late
Warm afternoon, but always touched with sun,
Wandering in the air
Of other summers, through the small blue gate
That is no longer there.


## TO ANY GARDEN

Garden, grow,
    In clump and row,
Golden trumpet, branch of snow,
Bell of blue and drop of white,
Swelling with your fill of light.

Garden, show your shades of green,
Spires of green, and blades of green,
Crinkled leaves upon whose bed
Little yellow stars are spread.

Garden, grow,
Quick and slow,
Some surprise each morning show;
And lovely as your blue and gold,
Are the surprises you withhold.

## THE START

The spike of daffodil,
The blue drop of a squill,

The furry silky stud
Of the gray apple-bud,

The cress of unknown seeds,
The tight brown wallflower beads,

The crocus' purse of gold,
The crumpled primrose fold,

The polyanthus star
Of red and lilac: are

The tiny treasury
Set on bush and tree

And printed on the ground
Which I this morning found.

Shall I, can I, when
At midsummer again

The fruit is set, and on
Each clump the flower new-blown

Swells the garden's store,
Love rose and apple more?


## THE FIRST BLACKBIRD

I've heard him, my first blackbird,
Practising at seven
Smatterings of phrases
That in May he raises
In his leafy heaven.
Turning all these stray
Fragments into praises
Of the breaking day.

Mist hung like a curtain
Across the breaking day.
There was scarcely light enough
To stir a bird to song,
It would not be bright enough
All the morning long
To make the blackie certain
That Spring was on its way.

Yet there he was, my blackbird,
Whistling like a lover
Little phrases, thrilling
Once again my willing
Memory to recover
In his broken lay
All our English songbirds trilling
In the breaking day.

## HOUSE HUNTERS

Birds will be house-hunting
  Soon—think of that!
Crows in the elm-tops
  And larks on the flat,
Owls in the belfry
  And wrens in the leaves,
And swifts will go house-hunting
  Under the eaves.

Moor-hen will hunt for her
  House in the reeds,
Chaffinch the apple-tree
  Bough ere she breeds,
Thrush in the hollow oak,
  Sparrow won't care—
Here, there, and everywhere,
  Any old where!

Cuckoo won't trouble,
  She'll just stop and call,
But starling and nightingale,
  Blackbird and all,
Jays as they chatter,
  And doves as they croon,
Soon will be house-hunting,
  Think of it—soon!

## HEIGH-HO, APRIL!

Heigh-ho!
Let the wind blow!
Let the frost glitter, and let the rain flow!
Primula's peeping,
And scilla's done weeping,
And daffodil's keeping the border aglow.
Buds on the lilac are starting to think,
Buds on the apple are stippled with pink,
Buds on the cherry are very near due,
Buds on the pear-tree have almost come through.

So heigh-ho!
Let the rain fall,
Let April shiver within a lace shawl!
Wallflower is breaking,
And tulip is waking
And arabis shaking her snow on the wall.
Fan of the lupin is spread like a star,
Blade of the iris stands up like a spar,
Spear of the hyacinth shatters the shield
That hardened the bosom of garden and field.


## LEAVES

Now when a branch hangs out its leaves
   Between the earth and sun
Through every rib and vein of green
   The light of day will run.

The leaves are not yet curtains
   Drawn when the sun's too bright,
Each leaf is still a little lamp
   That holds its fill of light.

## THE PEAR TREE

That pear tree, taller than the tiles,
Molded in solid creamy piles
Of blossom, like a goddess stands
Dropping beauty from her hands.

Her foot is on the grassy green,
Her head against blue sky is seen,
She is not long for mortal sight
In this perfection of spring light.

But yearly, ere that form of snow
Vanishes, again I know
Beauty is herself the foam
The gods in heaven raised her from.

## GIRLS IN THE GARDEN

The maiden trees their locks to dress
In everybody's view,
Laburnum has her yellow tress,
And lilac has her blue.

Green England covers all her miles
With sweet and blossoming girls,
Through loosened locks laburnum smiles,
And lilac through thick curls.

There's scarce a garden in the town
Or in the village where
These girls hang not their tresses down
And know that they are fair.

## THE GARDEN IN THE DARK

The midnight that is neither light nor dark
Has stolen the garden's yellows, blues and reds;
The giant poplar now seems twice its mark
Reared up against the sky above the beds;
The stirless air
Seals shapeless groves of leaves no longer green;
Only on the young apple there
The clusters of the blossom, with a sheen
Pallid as moth-wings, float upon the eye
As though they had no contact with their tree,
And might at any moment rise and fly
Back to some distant star I cannot see.


## SWEET HERBS

What shall I plant in my little herb border?
Which of these hundred sweet names shall I order?
Mallow or Marjoram, Tansy or Rue,
Lovage or Hyssop, or Call-Me-To-You?

Thyme or Sweet Cicely, which shall I take?
Shall I plant Basil for Isabel's sake?
Betony, Bergamot, Orris, Vervain,
Chicory, Woodruff, or Elecampane?

Here's Lady's Mantle, and here is Old Man;
If I cannot plant all, I must plant what I can,
But their names throw me into delicious disorder!
What shall I plant in my little herb border?

## SUMMER FOUNTAINS

Now the mid-May brings
Darting sharp-edged wings
As the pointed swallow
Doth the blunt cuckoo follow.

And now the Garden grows
In pointed tiers; the rose
Sharpens her bud, the fine
Campanula's green line
Cuts upward past the thick
Clumped primroses, the quick
Columbines shake their spray
Higher every day,
And sheaves of iris now
Pass the low apple-bough.

On earth and in the skies
The summer fountains rise.


## LILLIPUT

I have a tiny rockery
Scarce bigger than my napkin.
  There
On inch-wide plateaux, peaks as high
As alps in elfland, wander rare
Woodlands of pearly saxifrage,
There stonecrop's greenest rapids spread
In spates of golden stars that wage
War for possession of each bed
With crimson-petaled daisy-trees,

And groves of sea-pinks coral-white,
There the pale rock-rose with each breeze
Sways perilously on its height
And into some unknown abyss
Lets fall a petal like a plate—
And there upon the precipice
The blue veronica in great
Forests climbs up and lifts its spires
Into the heavens it outvies:
Oh, what adventurous desires
Might be achieved there, were my size
That of the beetle in the grass!
What cliffs and caverns I might climb,
And through what dangerous beauty pass
To reach the mountain-top in time!
Even now where the rock-shadow broods,
Who knows what daring midgets stride,
Lost in gold rivers and blue woods
My pocket-handkerchief could hide?

## MORNING LIGHT

How beautiful! how beautiful!
    The dew is on the grass,
And all the roses' cups are full
    They spill it as I pass.

The sun is very bright, and yet
    The morning has no heat,
The pebbled path is silver-wet
    And oh, the air smells sweet!

It is as though I never smelt
    So sweet and fresh an air,

It is as though I never felt
  Such sunlight in my hair,

Or saw a diamond cobweb hang
  Its curtain at my door,
Or ever heard the bird that sang
  That lovely song before—

As though I saw, felt, smelt, and heard
  This morning in their prime
The web, the sun, the air, the bird,
  And all, for the first time!

## MOONLIGHT

Now—look!—the big moon shines,
  In the late hours,
Bright on the sleeping lines
  Of summer flowers,
And the rich grass is seen
  Under her light,
Some hue that is not green
  In the late night.
The air is still and hot,
  And the rose-spray,
As though it had forgot
  To clear away
Its sunny scent, leaves yet
  On the night-air
Some perfume to make sweet
  The moonlight there.
Thinking the world is hers,
  She'll lose so soon,
Only the white moth stirs
  Under the moon.

## MISSY SINKINS

Hey, Missy Sinkins,
Little Missy Sinkins,
In your pretty petticoats all cut in frilly pinkins,
Here you come a-tiptoeing along the garden border
Like a ballerina with her snowy skirts in order.

They call you Mrs. Sinkins—
Stuffy-Nonsense! pooh!
Nobody called Sinkins
Went and married you!
If any Mr. Sinkins
Whispered: Name the Day!
You'd only shake your fluffy skirts at him,
And dance away.

Yes, Missy Sinkins,
I know you're Missy Sinkins,
Girlishly enjoying still your peekin's and your prinkin's,
Goffering your crumpled skirts, putting off the kisses,
Laughing No no no no no! I will not be a Mrs.!

## AFTER RAIN

The rain is clinging to the round rose-cheek,
And the sweet clustered larkspur heads are wet,
Like dark blue crumpled butterflies grown weak
Beneath their watery load; a silver fret
Of dew is sprinkled on the lupin-leaf,
And its green star is at the center lit
By one bright diamond-drop, to shine a brief
Life out until the sun recaptures it.

## A DRAGON-FLY

When the heat of the summer
Made drowsy the land,
A dragon-fly came
And sat on my hand,
With its blue jointed body,
And wings like spun glass,
It lit on my fingers
As though they were grass.

## THE MARK

Whence came the crimson on the daisy's tip?
Whence came the spot upon the foxglove's lip?
Whence came the tenderest of purple veins
Which finer than a hair the wind-flower stains?

Whence came the silver bloom upon the moth?
How came the billow by its cream of froth,
The jay by the blue feather in his wing,
The clover-meadow by its greenest ring?

These were perfection. Then their Maker saw
Even in their stainlessness a flaw,
And so in each of them the thing appears
Which marks our perfect joy in them with tears.

## THE BELL IN THE LEAVES

Who rings the bell
  All among the green leaves,
Who rings the bell
  That brings the folk to prayer?
Can it be the starlings,
The blackbirds or the throstles
Set the bell a-ringing,
Swinging in the green leaves,
Like a strange bird singing
  In its leafy lair?
Can it be the wind
Rising and falling
Sets the bell a-calling
  High among the green?
Or the Angel Gabriel
Summoning the masses,
Pulling as he passes
  Radiant, unseen?
Who sets the bell
  Ringing in the air?—
"Come, people! come, people!
  Come from everywhere!
Listen to the green tree
  Calling you to prayer."


## AMBUSH

The spider in its web of gray
Scarce visible in brightest day,
Now lurks in ambush, like a spy,
To catch the unsuspicious fly.

Too soon, too soon the gauzy wings
Of fragile sun-delighting things
Destroyed in Autumn's shroud will lie
Woven to catch the summer fly.


## CHILLY DAWN

The garden-fence bedewed with the mist
Of the silver-frosted dawn,
The ladder left under the apple-tree,
And the child's ball on the lawn;

The cobwebs stretched from the Michaelmas bush
To the trellised palisade,
The head of the weeping ash in the sun,
And the foot sunk in the shade;

Everything standing very still,
Asleep in its own form,
And the nip of the autumn-tang in the air
That will soon be summer-warm.


## AUTUMN RAIN

The horses of the sun that played so long on hill and plain
Have frisked away with golden-braided tail and tossing mane.

September takes the streaming road again, and passes by
Driving the horses of the rain across the sultry sky.

Autumn her golden days like ears of grain may have to spend,
But her first portent is the rain that signals summer's end.

"Oh, never call me summer—summer's over, summer's done,
And I with driving rain will come, where summer drove the
    sun!"

## TO MICHAELMAS DAISIES

You at your loveliest to be known
Must be beheld at early dawn,
When the white misty dew is thrown
Across your bushes round the lawn,
And all your purples, dark and pale,
Are seen beneath the chilly spray
Which hangs like a Communion veil
Between your beauty and the day.

## AUTUMN CROCUS

Here be Naked Boys
From the autumn grass,
Babes that make no noise
As they come and pass.
In beauty, ah so tender,
With silver limbs so slender,
They wander on the fields of earth
So short a time, alas.
They linger in the meadows
Like spring's forgotten shadows,
The Naked Boys of Autumn,
The fragile babes that pass.

## GOSSAMER

To-day I broke a lovelier thing
Than the most precious piece of Ming,
Tore a design of airier grace
Than any scrap of Mechlin lace,
Pulled down a pile more marvelous
Than Gothic monks have left for us,
Destroyed a craft more exquisite
Than any silver-worker's bit
Of ancient art; no fine-blown glass
That which I shattered could surpass,
Cellini would have given his ears
Could he, by laboring for years,
Have been by curious toil delivered
Of what to-day at dawn I shivered.

Artist! had you not hung before
The opening of my garden-door
Your masterpiece stretched taut on air,
That silver web would still be there.


## THE SECOND BIRTH OF ROSES

Where the working bee still hums,
And wood wasps hover in the heat,
The second birth of roses comes
To make my autumn garden sweet.

The Glory hangs a creamy bower
About the door, above my head,
The single rose with scarlet flower
Burns brightly in the middle bed;

The fair Ophelia is in bud,
Pink Caroline rounds out her bowl,
In glow of coral, flame, and blood,
The garden gets its second soul.

## THE MELLOW TIME

Now the mellowest sun of all
    The year doth fall
Upon the crumbling wall
Where still the vine hangs out a few large rags
Of yellow leaves,
And earth receives
The rest, as every branch hauls down its flags.
The creeper reddens
    Upon the rusty brick,
The beech, even as it deadens,
Seems quick
With autumn light, that softens its slow death.
And one loose-petaled rose, amid the litter
Of the dismantled beds, one rose still sweeter
Than summer's was, gives out its perfect breath.

## THE ELM-TREE

One November morning clean and cold
The elm-tree still was heavy with her gold,
Though beech and oak and aspen stripped and bare
Lifted their leafless branches in the air.

Then something happened, and her golden dress
The noble elm shook from her nakedness;

Yes, in a single hour, like a great rain,
She gave back all her leaves to earth again.


## THE TIRED TREE

In the soft earth the tips
  Already show:
Green bulbs and spears and slips,
  Promising oh
Such yellow daffodils,
  Tulips so bright,
Snowdrops with double frills
  Of green and white,
Crocus of mauve and gold,
  And scilla blue,
Unfolding as of old,
  And always new.
And pushed aside, forgot,
  A tiny tree
In its December pot
  Still here I see.
Its needles dusty are,
  Its silver chain
And tarnished tinsel star
  Past use again.
How tawdry you appear,
  Small tree, to-day,
While knob and spire and spear
  Grow green and gay;
Yet children who, for glee
  Of flowers, cry "Oh!"
Cried "Oh!" at you, tired tree,
  A month ago.
Come, I'll undress you now.
  Your hour is dead;

I will unwind each bough
    Of silver thread,
For knob and spear and spire
    Shine in the sun,
And you must to my fire—
    The party's done.


## THE BONFIRE

This cloud of smoke in other hours
Was leaves and grass, green twigs and flowers.

This bitter-sweet dead smell that blows
Was once the breathing of the rose.

Shapeless the forms of petals fair
And slender leaves melt on the air,

And in a scent she never knew
In life, the rose departeth too.


## BURNING THE GATE

We're burning up the old blue garden gate,
The little gate as old as dead Queen Anne,
That stood between the small ground and the great,
The gardens of the master and the man.

After two centuries the blue gate stumbled
Betwixts its posts, and hung and swung askew,
The slats were worm-eaten, the paint was crumbled,
And it must be replaced by something new.

The angry hand that pushed it is forgotten,
The tender, hesitating hand about
Its latch was dust before the latch was rotten—
Now even those old touches are burned out.

Yes, now the flame is turning it to ash,
All goings and all comings by its way
Are smoking up the chimney, and a flash
Of fire wipes out two centuries in a day.

# Joan's Door

# PANTOMIME

"How lovely!" said one little girl.
　　"How lovely!" said t'other,
As the scenes in the Pantomime whirl
　　Melted into each other.

How lovely the Principal Boy
　　With his wonderful dresses,
And his Ladylove born to enjoy
　　The most golden of tresses!

How lovely the dream still to be!
　　They will dream of it after—
And how lovely past all else to me
　　The little girls' laughter!


# SPRING IN HAMPSTEAD

Now all the crab-trees are in bloom,
　　And all the may-trees are so white,
The Heath is like the loveliest room
　　For us to play in with delight.

There's little sunken birchwoods, and
　　Small precipices just beyond,
And secret creeks, and plots of sand,
　　And on the top a shining pond,

Where little boats sail to and fro,
　　And dogs get wet, and children run,
And like the crab-trees down below
　　Life blossoms sweetly in the sun.

## SNOW IN THE GARDEN

Here's the soft snow again.
   See now, once more,
Drifts at the window-pane,
   Drifts by the door.

Run for your wooden spade,
   Which it may be
Silver-sand castles made,
   Drowned by the sea.

Build now your tower here;
   Let it be done
Ere it shall disappear
   Drowned by the sun.

All our best castles and
   Towers end so,
Builders in silver-sand,
   Dreamers in snow!

## CIRCUS

The brass band blares,
The naphtha flares,
The sawdust smells,
Showmen ring bells,
And oh! right into the circus ring
Comes such a lovely, lovely thing,
A milk-white pony with flying tress,
And a beautiful lady,
A beautiful lady,
A *beautiful* lady in a pink dress!

A red-and-white clown
For joy tumbles down,
Like a pink rose
Round she goes
On her tip-toes
With the pony under—
And then, oh, wonder!
The pony his milk-white tresses **droops,**
And the beautiful lady,
The *beautiful* lady,
Flies like a bird through the paper **hoops!**
Then he waggles his feet and stands on his **head,**
And the little boys on the twopenny seats
Scream with laughter and suck their sweets.


## JOAN'S DOOR

Once I had a green door
   As little as could be,
It was just as high as you
   And half as high as me.

YOU walked through the green door
   As upright as you please,
But I had to crawl
   On my hands and my knees.

I said the little green door
   Was my very own,
But you said, "It's Joan's door!"
   And walked through alone.

If now we found our green door
   Once and for all,

YOU couldn't walk through
  We'd both have to crawl.

If it wasn't my door,
  Would it now be yours?
Have you lost your right, Joan,
  To little green doors?

To call that little green door
  Your very own door
You shouldn't be eleven, Joan,
  You ought to be four.


## THE CRACK OF LIGHT

"No," the little girl said,
As she snuggled down in bed,
"I don't have a night-light lit,
I'm not afraid a bit.

"But when you've got to go
Leave the door open *so*
With just a crack of light—
Yes," she said, *"that's* right!"

Down the stairs I went
And left her there content—
But oh, what happened then
She never told again.

She for her secret kept
What happened while she slept,
And what came at night
Through the crack of light.

## THE OLD MAN'S TOES

Up the street
Down the street,
My
   Joan
       goes—
(Mind you don't tread
   upon the
Old
    Man's
         Toes!)
She hops along the
   pavements
Into every Square,
But she mustn't touch
   the Cracks in
   between
Them
     There.
The Squares on the pavement
Are safe
       as can
           be;
One is the Sands
By the side
       of the
          sea;
One is a Garden where
Joan's
    flowers
        grow;
One is a Meadow
She
   and I
      know.

But the Cracks are *dangerous*,
As
   Everybody
         knows!
The Cracks in the Pavement are the
Old
   Man's
        Toes.
And one who treads on the
Old
   Man's
       Corn
Will wish in a jiffy he had
Never
    been
       born!
For the Sea will roll up and
Suck
   you
      down!
And a horrid blight will turn your
Garden
      brown!
And into the Meadow with an
Angry
   *Moo*
A Big Cross Cow will come
Rushing
    at
      You!
*Up* the street and down the street
My
   Joan
     goes—
Here she makes a Pudding,
There she smells a Rose,

Yonder she goes stooping where the
Mushroom
         grows—
(Mind, Joan! don't tread upon the
Old
    Man's
        Toes!)

## THE LOST FARTHING

Oh, she has dropped her farthing, her farthing in the street!
She *saw* her brand-new farthing drop down beside her feet;
She *saw* her farthing rolling like a little wheel of gold,
But she hasn't got the least idea how far her farthing rolled.

Policeman, stop the traffic
        A-covering the ground,
And don't let anybody move
        Until her farthing's found.
Oh, is it on the pavement
        Or in the gutter cold?
There isn't any saying
        How far her farthing rolled.

Lord Mayor, ride through London
        And send the word around
That all the city gates be shut
        Until her farthing's found.
Does Whitechapel, or Ludgate,
        Or Bow her treasure hold?
There isn't any saying
        How far her farthing rolled.

King of England, waken!
        Let all your trumpets sound,
Bidding your seaports to be shut

Until her farthing's found.
Oh, is it in the Yorkshire dales
      Or on the Kentish wold?
There isn't any saying
      How far her farthing rolled.

Oh, *dear,* she's dropped her farthing! She *heard* it drop, she
    said;
The baker gave it her for change when she went to fetch
    the bread,
And she was running to the shop where sugar mice are sold
When she dropped her brand-new farthing, and didn't see
    where it rolled.


## THE SWEETSTUFF WIFE

The Sweetstuff Wife in the queer little shop
      Has four little window-panes
With bottles of bulls-eye and lollipop,
Peardrop, lemon drop, chocolate drop,
      Boxes of gay tin trains,
Comfits of every colour too,
With mottos on them, like "I Love You"
And "Do You Love Me?" "Be Kind," "Be True,"
      And horses with fluffy manes,
And sawdust dollies with china heads,
And painted tea-sets, and tiny beds,
And balls with quarters of blues and reds,
      And butterfly aeroplanes,
And sugar biscuits, and sweet cigars,
And ninepins, and wind-up motor-cars,
And masks and crackers and silver stars
      And paper flowers and chains.

The Sweetstuff Wife is never quite done
Cramming her windows full of fun,

She must *like* making it nice for one,
      She takes such heaps of pains!
And even if you haven't a penny
(And where she lives there are none too many)
      She never, never complains
Of the big round eyes fixed on this and that
And the small round noses pressed so flat
      On the four little window-panes.
So I think you would surely find
      That the queer little Sweetstuff Wife
Once swallowed a comfit that said "Be Kind,"
      And *was,* for the rest of her life.


## A WISH

If I had a wish—
Well, *what* would I wish?
For a Crimson Cat,
Or a Purple Fish,
Or a Green Top-Hat,
Or Scarlet Butter,
Or something like that!—
You'll say what utter
Waste of a perfectly splendid Wish!
Because you're content with the same sort of dish
Day after day, and would wish, I guess,
For a little *more* Pudding, or one *more* Dress.
But I mean to say,
If a Wish by strange
Chance came my way,
I'd have a change;
And for *real* delight
I'd see it was spent
On something quite
*Quite*
      Different!

## CITY STREETS AND COUNTRY ROADS

The city has streets—
　　But the country has roads.
In the country one meets
　　Blue carts with their loads
Of sweet-smelling hay,
　　And mangolds, and grain:
Oh, take me away
　　To the country again!

In the city one sees,
　　Big trams rattle by,
And the breath of the chimneys
　　That blot out the sky,
And all down the pavements
　　Stiff lamp-posts one sees—
But the country has hedgerows,
　　The country has trees.

As sweet as the sun
　　In the country is rain:
Oh, take me away
　　To the country again!


## EVENING HUSHES

Evening hushes
The thoughts of the Poplars, the dreams of the Rushes.

## KINGFISHER

A flicker of blue
Under the sallows—
Over the shallows
A Kingfisher flew!

## DOVES AND STARLINGS

The Doves say "Green Leaves!"
  In tones soft and shady;
The Starlings "Green Peas!"
  So merry and greedy.

"Green Leaves! green Leaves!
See how the sun weaves
In, out, over, and through
Our lovely green tree,
Till his spots of gold dew
Fall on You,
            And on Me."

"Green Peas! green Peas
Are better than these!
Look! all down the rods
In the garden I see
The fat, swelling pods
For You,
            And for Me!"

"Green Peas!" chuckles Starling.
  "Green Leaves!" coos the Dove,
"Green leaves for my darling,
  My dear and my love."

## SEVEN-SISTERS ROSES

Seven white sisters
All in a bunch—
Mother, let's ask them
In to lunch.

Nay, they're not used
To our clumsy fare!
They eat the sunshine
And drink the air.

Seven white sisters,
Enjoy your meal—
But *I* want something
Much more real!

I have no knife
That would cut the sun,
Out of my cup
The wind would run.

Eat up your feast
With your lips of silk,
While I run in
To my bread-and-milk.

## OH, HARK!

Oh, hark, my darling, hark!
I hear the owl in the dark,
The white, low-flying owl
Along the air doth prowl
With her strange, lonely wail.

And hark, my darling, hark!
I hear the stars in the dark,
I hear the singing sky
Shaking with melody!—
   It is the nightingale.


## BLOW THE STARS HOME

Blow the Stars home, Wind, blow the Stars home
Ere Morning drowns them in golden foam.


## FOR A COCK

Strutting cock, with swelling chest,
   Stepping on your scaly legs
Past the warm and busy nest
   Where the worried hens lay eggs,
Why do *you,* I'd like to know,
   Strut and crow and swagger so?

Do you really think, I beg,
   When the sun swims into view,
That it is a yellow egg
   Which has just been laid by you?—
Only laying little moons.


## SUN AND WIND

The old sun, the gold sun,
   With lovely May returning,
Went among the chestnut trees
   And set their candles burning.

The cold winds, the bold winds,
    Came down like Goths and Vandals,
And went among the chestnut trees
    Blowing out their candles.

## TREASURE

What have you picked up, baby on the shore?
Such treasure as was never found before!
        A pebble white as snow
        And one as round as O!
        A curly, yellow shell,
        One flat and pink as well;
        A crab, a tinier thing
        Than daddy's signet-ring;
        A bit of glass so blue
        The sky cannot look through;
        And seaweed green as cress,
        And soft as mother's tress.

Carry them home and strew them on the floor—
To-morrow you can run and get some more.

## WINDFALLS

Windfalls under the apple-trees!
Eat as many as you please.
Any apple that still lies
Shall be turned to apple-pies;
But the apple on the bough that stays
Shall be stored in the loft for winter days.

## PENCIL AND PAINT

Winter has a pencil
For pictures clear and neat,
She traces the black tree-tops
Upon a snowy sheet,
But autumn has a palette
And a painting-brush instead,
And daubs the leaves for pleasure
With yellow, brown, and red.

## FOR A CLOUD

If I could only be a cloud,
Wouldn't I be proud
To be what I pleased as the wind blows!
For very often I would be
A mackerel in the sea
Or else a flock of sheep as the wind blows.

Sometimes I'd be a flying swan,
And sometimes sail upon
The sky like a ship as the wind blows;
Sometimes I'd be a drift of snow,
Sometimes a lamp aglow
To shine in the dawn as the wind blows.

If only I could be a cloud,
I'd laugh, laugh aloud,
And be a thousand things as the wind blows!—
But since a little boy am I,
I can only be a man as the wind blows.

## RAINBOW

Oh, my pretty rainbow!
My pretty, pretty rainbow!

At six o'clock in summer
    As I lay in my bed,
A cloud shed a tear,
    And then the sun shed
A smile; and an arc
    Of blue light and red,
And daffodil-yellow
    Shone on my bed.

"Oh, my rainbow!
    My rainbow!" I said,
And leaned out of window
    To go where it led;
But before I could follow
    My rainbow had fled,
And my mother came running,
    And put me back to bed.

Oh, my rainbow!
My pretty, pretty rainbow!
Was it really dead?

## BROKEN WING

We found a little bird in spring
    New-fallen from its nest,
It had a pretty broken wing
    And a small hurt on its breast.

We took it home and laid it soft
   In flannel and green grass,
The milk and crumbs we brought it oft
   It could not eat, alas!

It was too young to pipe aloud,
   It was too hurt to fly,
The grass and flannel were its shroud
   When it came to die.

## NEARLY

Into the room
I crept so soft—
I scarcely breathed,
And I never coughed—
So soft, they could hardly
Know I was there,
Into the room
With oh, such care
I crept—that I *nearly*
Broke their Law,
They were just in time,
But I *nearly* Saw!

Out in the dark
I stood so still—
Like a bit of the door
Or the window-sill—
So still, they could hardly
Think of me,
Out in the dark
So noiselessly
I stood—that I *nearly*

Got the Word,
They were just in time,
But I *nearly* Heard!

Down in the wood
I tried so hard,
Hoping to get them
Off their guard,
So hard, they could scarcely
Get away,
Down in the wood
So *hard* that day
I tried—that I *nearly*
Got right through,
They were just in time,
But I *nearly* knew!


## FOR A DEWDROP

Small shining drop, no lady's ring
Holds so beautiful a thing.
At sun-up in the early air
The sweetness of the world you snare.
Within your little mirror lie
The green grass and the winged fly;
The lowest flower, the tallest tree
In your crystal I can see.
Why, in your tiny globe you hold
The sun himself, a midge of gold.
It makes me wonder if the world
In which so many things are curled,
The world which all men real call,
Is not the real world at all,
But just a drop of dew instead
Swinging on a spider's thread.

## THE TALE OF LILLA

Lilla was as fair a child
As any mother's child could be
That in a valley-wood ran wild
   And learned and loved each tree.

Her home was in an orchard found
Of apple-trees of every kind,
But all must cross the forest-ground
   Lilla's small house to find—

Must push his way through ash and oak,
Holly and chestnut, thorn and beam,
And pass below the beech-tree's cloak,
   And through the birch-tree's dream.

One morning, one of all the trees
That loved her so it could not part
With her, stretched out its arms to seize
   And shut her in its heart.

Her toes it hid in little roots,
Her body in the narrow stem,
Her fingers in the leafy shoots
   Moved when the wind moved them;

Her hair like golden moss did creep
And cling about the twisted boughs,
The tears her two blue eyes did weep
   Oozed down her woody house.

Her Mother through the wood did run,
And "Lilla! Lilla!" she did call,
"Oh, Lilla!" in the setting sun,
    "My Lilla!" at starfall.

She met a Wise-Witch wild and strange
Gathering gossamers from the thorn.
"Oh, have you seen the fairest child
    Of any mother born?

"She was the lightest, happiest thing,
She looked like daisies on the green,
My Lilla laughed as robins sing,
    Oh, tell me! have you seen?"

"I have not seen, and yet I see,
For I am wise of bad and good.
She is fast shut inside a tree
    That grows in your own wood;

"And not until the tree is hewn
And burned upon a woodman's fire
Will you behold 'neath sun or moon
    The child of your desire."

"Oh, which tree is my darling's bed
Of all that tread the forest floor?"
But the old Wise-Witch shook her head
    And would say nothing more.

Home ran the Mother to her man
And told him of the woman's tale.
"Go hew the timber, all you can,
    That grows within the vale!

"Take your sharp axe to yonder trees,
And strike down aspen, ash, and beech—
Lilla may be in none of these,
    Yet she may be in each.

"She loved the oak-tree's rugged root,
She loved the chestnut's yellow roof,
She loved the elm's big shaggy foot
    Like a farm-horse's hoof;

"But we will burn the forest down
From noble crest to brush so mean,
Until the green-leaved trees turn brown
    And brown turn back to green,

"We'll burn the forest year by year
Until it is a barren plain,
We'll burn it till we get our dear,
    Our Lilla, back again!"

The woodman took his sharpest axe
And laid the trees down on the earth,
And cut them up in kindling stacks,
    And burned them on his hearth;

Oak, ash, and elm he overcast,
He felled both birch and beech, but oh!
He could not cut the trees as fast
As other trees did grow.

He burned the forest year by year
He could not make that wood a plain,
He hewed the trees to find his dear,
    And hewed the trees in vain.

And when his old wife died, and he
Died too from being left alone,
Though many knew the tale, the tree
   Of Lilla was not known.

Long afterwards, so very long
That Lilla was a fairy tale,
Another woodman young and strong
   Lived in the forest vale;

And one day in a summer storm
When lightning came in flashes fleet,
One struck his oldest apple's form
   And laid it at his feet.

Next day he dragged the fallen tree
Hard by the shed that stacked his wood.
"Come a cold winter night," said he,
   "This will burn sweet and good."

That winter-time he warmed his feet
And hands beside his apple fire,
Its flame was bright, its smoke was sweet
   As any could desire.

Night after night the apple-flash
Of red and gold did dance and leap,
Dawn after dawn the apple-ash
   Lay in a rising heap;

And one night happened when he cast
A mossy twig on as he turned
To sleep. "There, that's," he said, "the last—
   Now all the apple's burned."

Next morning in the winter dark
The woodman rose up in his room,
And saw by his one candle-spark
   A small form in the gloom:

A little form, old, old and grey,
Where the red flames had ceased to flash
Like a sweet withered apple lay
   Among the old grey ash.

She lay as though asleep on down,
She never wakened, though she smiled,
She was from tiptoe to her crown
   No bigger than a child.

"The night," he said, "has driven her in,
And here her rest the old thing found,"
He took his spade and did begin
   To dig the frosty ground,

And at the orchard's farthest edge
Where the first golden aconite
Would hang its ball beneath the hedge,
   He laid her out of sight.

And who she was, and whence she came,
And what her age, and where she grew,
And what her nation and her name,
   The woodman never knew.

She slept. And still the fairy tale
Of Lilla wanders far and free,
And many a child in many a vale
   Wonders "Which tree? which tree?"

## CITY-UNDER-WATER

Maureen came out of Ireland with her double-cutting
     tongue.
She was crusty with the older folk, but easy with the young.
She gave my Mother answers back my Mother thought too
     free,
But Maureen gave nothing else but songs and fairy tales to
     me.

She told me of a lovely lake—in her own land, she said—
With a City-Under-Water lying sunken on its bed.
Sometimes, she said, you'd surely hear the church-bells ring-
     ing good
And clear right from the bottom to the top, indeed you
     would.

She tucked me up and left me after pulling up the blind,
And City-Under-Water kept on running in my mind.
She pulled my blind because, if I was anything like *her*,
I'd find the stars were worth considering, indeed they were.

I looked out through the window where the stars looked in
     again,
And the sky spread like a dark blue lake across the window-
     pane.
I thought that I was looking down instead of looking up,
And the silver stars were swarming at the bottom of a cup.

I saw bright spires and shining streets and tall and glittering
     towers,
And trees with silver cherries on and silver cherry-flowers,
And silver swallows flying where the silver fishes slid,
And silver churchbells ringing good and clear, indeed they
     did.

Next day I told my Mother, and I told my Maureen too,
I'd seen City-Under-Water, Mother said it wasn't true,
I'd had a dream. But *Maureen* said, sure, did I think
    because
I'd dreamed about a thing it wasn't true? Indeed it was.


## THE WONDERFUL CLOCK

I saw the clock in Wells
    Which an old monk made to chime,
With a doll to ring the bells
    And a star to tell the time,
With knights to tilt the hour
    From noon round to noon,
And the minutes in the power
    Of the sun and moon.


## THE KERRY LOON

As I walked on the Hills of Kerry
    I saw a wee green Loon
Sat drinking under a blackthorn bush
    From the horn of this month's moon.

At his pointed feet all round about
    The young moons' horns did lie
With every silver drop run out,
    For he had licked them dry.

At his right hand still mounting up
    The half-moons made a heap,
But empty was each yellow cup
    For he had drunk so deep.

The bladders of the full moon, thin
  And smooth, on his left hand rose,
But he had sucked each golden skin,
  And was long-done with those.

Oh, all the moons of all-time
  Were drained by the Kerry Loon
That I saw under a blackthorn bush
  Drinking of this month's moon.

## CREEPING JENNY

Creeping Jenny,
Why so shy?
I can hear you
Creeping by!
Quieter than a
Harvest mouse,
Or small rain-drops
On a house,
Or green beetles
In the grass,
Creeping Jenny,
Though you pass—
Every footstep
I can hear,
I have got so
Fine an ear!
I can hear the
Pinecones shut
I can hear the
Growing nut,
I can hear the
Cloud go by

In the highest
Of the sky,
I can hear the
Shadow fall
Of an apple
On my wall,
I can hear a
Sunbeam hum,
I can hear the
Twilight come.
Creeping Jenny,
How can you
Think I will not
Hear you too?
My door's waiting,
Lift the pin—
Don't creep by, Jenny,
Creep in.


## RAGGED ROBIN

O my Robin, Robin in rags!
O my Robin of jags and tags!
Whichever way the old world wags
  I'll love my Ragged Robin O!

Sweet William stands in a garden
His dress is always neat and trim
But better far than I love him
  I love my Ragged Robin O!

With stitchwort I will darn his holes,
With cuckoo-shoes I'll patch his soles,
And when the trembling harebell tolls
  I'll wed my Ragged Robin O!

While other men their hours employ,
We'll run the way of Traveller's Joy
By hedgerow, wood, and lane, my boy,
    My laughing Ragged Robin O!

We'll dine on song and sup on verse
And when things go from bad to worse
We'll borrow from the Shepherd's Purse
    A trifle, Ragged Robin O!

And he the gayest lad that thrives,
And I the merriest of wives,
We'll live our tattered summer lives,
    I and my Ragged Robin O!

O my Robin, Robin in rags!
O my Robin of jags and tags!
Whichever way our fortune wags,
    I'll love my Ragged Robin O!


## WILD THYME

Time runs wild on the hilltops,
    Time walks tame in the valleys,
Time runs wild with Gypsy Nan,
    But oh! goes tame with Alice.

Night and day on the hilltops
    Are one to the Gypsy child,
She eats her breakfast by the moon
    Up there where time runs wild.

Alice, meek in the valleys,
  Lives by her mother's plan.—
"O Alice, run on the hills with me,
  Run wild with Gypsy Nan.

"You shall lie and sleep in the sunlight
  While your playmates sit in school,
And when they lie beneath the sheets
  You shall dance with stars in a pool.

"You shall dream most when you're waking,
  You shall learn most when you play,
You will never think of to-morrow
  Or remember yesterday.

"You shall eat when you will and go where you will,
  For all folk follow their wills
Who leave their ticking clocks to live
  With the wild time on the hills.

"For time runs wild on the hilltops,
  And time walks tame in the valleys."—
"I thank you kindly, Gypsy Nan,
  I'll stay where I am," said Alice.


### PENNY ROYAL

Penny, Penny Royal,
  As gold as any Pound!
The Penny is the royalest coin
  On Tom Tiddler's Ground.
A Penny is sufficient

For anybody's fun—
'Twill buy a stick of liquorice,
   Or a currant bun,
'Twill buy a paper windmill
   To turn as you run,
'Twill buy a big glass marble
   Or a small pop-gun,
'Twill buy a jolly bus-ride
   That's very soon done,
'Twill buy a beggar's blessing
   On the King's own son.
I picked up a Penny
   On Tom Tiddler's Ground,
Penny, Penny Royal—
   A fig for your Pound!

## MORNING GLORY

Oh, did your Granny sing the song,
   Or did your Nanny tell the story,
Of little Tom who all night long
   Waited to see the Morning Glory?

He watched until the blackest hour
   Had changed into a shining whiteness,
The sky was like an opening flower
   With pinky streaks upon the brightness.

The sun was like a trumpet-call
   That set all earth and heaven ringing,
The fields were lakes of gold, and all
   The rising larks were angels singing.

The trees had wings instead of leaves,
  The air with drops of song was spangled,
And on the thread the spider weaves
  Small silver stars in millions dangled.

The little rosy clouds uncurled
  Like blossoms for the day's adorning,
And little Tom beheld the world
  In all the glory of the morning.

But Tom was only nine hours old
  So could not tell it to another;
The Morning Glory, never told,
  Was Tom's first secret with his Mother.


## OUR MOTHER'S TUNES

Our Mother sang tunes
We heard from no other,
Sweet Darky melodies,
Strange Irish croons,
Oh, sing again, Mother,
Sing us those tunes!

Some we forget,
And others somehow
Half are remembered
And half slip us yet.
Dear Mother, sing now
The tunes we forget!

For you and no other
Can sing us them, Mother.

## FIE, FIE!

Fie, fie!
Rockaby!
Babes must sleep, they must not cry.

## THE BELLS IN THE VALLEY

The Bells in the Valley
Are ringing for Sally.
The Bells on the Hill
Are ringing for Will.
The Valley says "Shall I?"
"You Will!" says the Hill.

## GROUNDSEL

Groundsel!
Groundsel!
A handsel, a handsel
For your Bird in the Cage I
cry—
Oh, let the Bird fly, and you
never need buy
Groundsel!

## DOWN! DOWN!

Down, down!
Yellow and brown
The leaves are falling over the town.

## ECONOMY

Until I can earn me a Shilling a year
I'll go in Silk because Satin is dear.

## ECHO! ECHO!

O Echo, Echo,
        all over the Water,
All over the Water,
        have you seen my Daughter,
Have you seen my Daughter
        who went for to pick O
To pick O herb-willow,
        herb-willow, O Echo?

## THE ARCHER

I'll shoot an arrow, an arrow, an arrow!
If I miss an Eagle, I might hit a Sparrow;
If I miss a Sparrow, I might hit a Tit;
If I miss a Tit, I am certain to hit
        *Some*-thing!

## GIRLS A-WEEPING

*Girls a-weeping*
*For their boys a-sleeping*
Wake, Boys, wake,
For the Girls' sake!

Why do you sleep
So long and deep
All the day
When you might play,
All the night
When you might delight?
But the Boys lie still,
Sleeping their fill.


## THE WITCH! THE WITCH!

The Witch! the Witch! don't let her get you!
Or your Aunt wouldn't know you the next time she met
    you!


## GRAND-DADS

Grand-Dads
Only Hobble.
Fathers walk exactly double.
Big boys, big boys, big boys, big
    boys
Run like hares and never trouble.
Little boys, little boys, little boys, little
    boys,
Little boys caper as light as a bubble.—
*But*
Grand-Dads
Only Hobble.

## TWO PENN'ORTH OF CHESTNUTS

Two penn'orth of Chestnuts!
Two penn'orth of Chestnuts!
If they come from Spain
You may take them back again!
If they come from Italy
I'll refuse them bitterly!
But if they come from Houghton Wood
I'll know they are little and sweet and good.


## FAIRIES

Don't go looking for fairies,
   They'll fly away if you do.
You never can see the fairies
   Till they come looking for you.


## INVITATION TO A MOUSE

There's pudding in the pantry,
   There's jam upon the shelf,
There's bacon in a pastry pie
   On a dish of delf—
Mousiekin, wee Mousiekin,
   Go and help yourself!
But please, Mousie, please,
Don't touch the toasted cheese,
For if you do mayhap
Something will go snap!
And the pudding and the jam
And the pastry and the ham
Will have to stay untasted, all wasted on the shelf.

## BABY STANDS

Look! my baby's standing there
With her hands upon the chair.

Suddenly she lifts her hands,
And one wondrous moment stands

Bright-eyed, flushed, surprised and sweet,
On her two unsteady feet.

Down she goes, then—down she goes!
Oh, but how she laughs and crows,

Laughs and crows as though to say,
She *did* take her hands away!

## MARMALADE

I simply can't *tell* you how glad I am
When the Marmalade is Apricot Jam!

## RHYME

Two legs will bear a marching man
Swifter than one leg ever can;
Two horses draw a lady's carriage
Gayer than one to church and marriage;
Two wings will lift a flying swallow
Where lame-winged birds can never follow—
So Poetry, when its two lines chime,
Move swift, and gay, and light with Rhyme.

## THE DAISIES

The rich and rare magnolia tree
  Has one white flower
Which blossoms in a single hour.
But in the common grass, oh, see!
  Daisies are found
In thousands near the whole year round.

In the great palace with its wall,
  Only one queen
At one time in the land is seen;
But in the thousand streets, look, all
  Running there wild,
Plays every common mother's child.

## THE BRIDE

In she goes
In a veil of white,
Her face is morning,
Her eyes are light,
Her step might be
The step of a flower—
In she goes
In her beautiful hour,
Little girls, pretty girls, love her, do!
You shall wear white veils one day too.

Out she comes
In a ring of gold,
Her face is pale
And her hands are cold,

But her smile, her smile!—
Oh, what can it mean?
Where has she been,
And what has she seen?
Little girls, pretty girls, kiss her, do!
You shall wear gold rings one day too.


## FOR GOOD MORNING

Good-Morning now.
Wake, body,
Wake, mind!
Work, play,
Seek, find,
Eat breakfast,
Dinner too,
Wash, brush,
Sing, dance, and do!
Good-morning now.


## FOR GOOD-NIGHT

Now good-night.
Fold up your clothes
As you were taught,
Fold your two hands,
Fold up your thought;
Day is the plough-land,
Night is the stream,
Day is for doing
And night is for dream.
Now good-night.

# THE HILLS OVER THE WATER

The hills lie over the water
  With the golden seas between,
And the boats go over the water
  To the hills so dimly seen,
To the hills that lie in a magic mist
  Past a sea with a magic sheen.

I will take a boat over the water,
  I will cross the sea of gold
And enter into the hills of mist.
  Yet I know, without being told,
    That they will not be
    The hills I see,
The blue hills over the water
  Lying there fold on fold.

I shall look back over the water
  To my own deserted shore,
And over the magic water
  See magic hills once more,
Hills that I walked in yesterday
  Yet never saw before.

# Come Christmas

# IN THE WEEK WHEN
# CHRISTMAS COMES

This is the week when Christmas comes.

Let every pudding burst with plums,
And every tree bear dolls and drums,
  In the week when Christmas comes.

Let every hall have boughs of green,
With berries glowing in between,
  In the week when Christmas comes.

Let every doorstep have a song
Sounding the dark street along,
  In the week when Christmas comes.

Let every steeple ring a bell
With a joyful tale to tell,
  In the week when Christmas comes.

Let every night put forth a star
To show us where the heavens are,
  In the week when Christmas comes.

Let every stable have a lamb
Sleeping warm beside its dam,
  In the week when Christmas comes.

This is the week when Christmas comes.

## EARTH AND SKY

*(They talk to each other on Christmas Eve.)*

| | |
|---|---|
| *Earth.* | Oh Sky, you look so drear! |
| *Sky.* | Oh Earth, you look so bare! |
| *Earth.* | How chilly you appear! |
| *Sky.* | How empty you lie there! |

| | |
|---|---|
| *Sky.* | My winds blow icy cold. |
| *Earth.* | My flowers have gone from me. |
| *Sky.* | Yet I've one Star of gold. |
| *Earth.* | And I have one green Tree. |

*Sky.*  
I'll set my Star on high  
Alone in its own light  
For any Child to spy  
Who wakes on Christmas Night.

*Earth.*  
I'll hang my Tree with toys,  
Like fruit and flowers gay,  
For little girls and boys  
To pick on Christmas Day.

*They say together.*  
Then let the soft snow fall,  
And let the cold wind blow!  
We have in spite of all  
A pretty thing to show;

Yes, Christmas Eve and Morn  
We'll show our pretty thing  
To every baby born  
Of Beggar-man or King.

| | |
|---|---|
| *Earth.* | Oh Sky, you look so clear! |
| *Sky.* | Oh Earth, you look so fair! |
| *Earth.* | How bright your Star shines here. |
| *Sky.* | How green your Tree grows there. |

## SIX GREEN SINGERS

The frost of the moon fell over my floor
And six green singers stood at my door.

"What do ye here that music make?"
"Let us come in for Christ's sweet Sake."

"Long have ye journeyed in coming here?"
"Our Pilgrimage was the length of the year."

"Where do ye make for?" I asked of them.
"Our Shrine is a Stable in Bethlehem."

"What will ye do as ye go along?"
"Sing to the world an evergreen song."

"What will ye sing for the listening earth?"
"One will sing of a brave-souled Mirth,

"One of the Holiest Mystery,
The Glory of glories shall one song be,

"One of the Memory of things,
One of the Child's imaginings,

"One of our songs is the fadeless Faith,
And all are the Life more mighty than death."

"Ere ye be gone that music make,
Give me an alms for Christ's sweet Sake."

"Six green branches we leave with you;
See they be scattered your house-place through.

"The staunch blithe Holly your board shall grace,
Mistletoe bless your chimney-place.

"Laurel to crown your lighted hall,
Over your bed let the Yew-bough fall,

"Close by the cradle the Christmas Fir,
For elfin dreams in its branches stir,

"Last and loveliest, high and low,
From ceil to floor let the Ivy go."

From each glad guest I received my gift
And then the latch of my door did lift—

"Green singers, God prosper the song ye make
As ye sing to the world for Christ's sweet Sake."

## ROBIN TO JENNY

The frost is on the ground, Jenny,
   Too hard for bill to crack,
And where shall food be found, Jenny,
   That you and I now lack?
Oh, thanks be to the burrowing mole
   That still throws up his hill—
His fresh-turned earth's my goal, Jenny,
   And that will feed us still.

The ground is like a rock, Jenny,
   A rock I cannot break!
Poor Robin can't unlock, Jenny,
   Its larder for your sake;
So thanks be to the working-man
   That doth his garden till—
We from his furrow can, Jenny,
   Get that will feed us still.

The ground is hard as ice, Jenny,
   Of every comfort bare,
And where shall I look twice, Jenny,
   To get your daily fare?
Now thanks be to the girl or boy
   That strews the window-sill—
Come spring we'll sing them joy, Jenny,
   Because they fed us still.


## THE BROWN BIRDS

Scant is the holly,
The holly-berries few!
There's a bunch for the rich man
To see his Christmas through,
And a spray or a sprig
For the pretty-well-to-do,—
But what of the brown birds
Whom hunger maketh bold?
What of the poor birds
A-seeking in the cold?
Oh, when the holly's scant
And the holly-berries few,
What will the brown birds,
The poor birds do?

## A CHRISTMAS LULLABY

The sheep upon the mountain,
  The ram, the lamb, the ewe,
Are watching with their shepherd—
  And must thou needs watch too?
      Lullaby!
      Why, oh, why
Keep thy big eyes on the sky?
Is it to see a Star on high?
Starry eyes, go lullaby!

The trees along the valley,
  The holly, fir, and yew,
Are green with holy secrets—
  Hast thou a secret, too?
      Lullaby!
      Why, oh, why
Wilt thou never close thy eye?
Is it to see a Child go by?
Little child, go lullaby!


## ANNAR-MARIAR'S CHRISTMAS SHOPPING

Annar-Mariar-Elizar Smith
Looked in the Baker's window with
Her brother Willyum by the hand.
"Look!" she said, "Willyum! ain't it grand!
See them pudding's done up in basins—
They're all stuffed full of currints and raisins!
We'll 'ave that big 'un there, Willyum, see,

Fer dinner on Chrismuss Day, you an' me.
See them Chrismuss Cakes white and pink,
With holly and bells! Would you like, d'you think,
The one with the snowballs and funny man?
What, that with the robins? All right, you can."

Annar-Mariar-Elizar Smith
Stopped at the Greengrocer's, where the pith
Of its beautiful wonders were seen outside.
"Look at the Chrismuss-trees, duck!" she cried.
"Which'll we 'ave sent 'ome? That tall
'Un there'll do beautiful for us all!
And that little tiny'll be jest right
For Baby to see when she wakes at night.
We'll 'ave that bundle of 'olly, oo!
And that mistletoe there!—we'll tell 'em to
Send nuts, and bananers, and tangerines,
And apples, along o' the evergreens."

Annar-Mariar-Elizar Smith
Saw in the Toyshop a world of myth
And fairytale. "Oo!" she chuckled, "see
The dolls, and the crackers, and all! The tree
'Ll look lovely with some of them shiny things,
And the Fairy Queen with the silvery wings,
And the Father Chrismuss, and sparkly chains,
And the teaset fer me, and the box of trains
Fer you, and the farmyard fer Baby, wot?
Sha'n't we serprise 'er with all we've got!"
Then Annar and Willyum home did run
With the whole of their Christmas shopping done.

## THROUGH A SHOP WINDOW

How full the glittering shops are now
   With chattering tongues and open purses,
And children scrambling anyhow
   Beside their mothers, aunts, and nurses;
With eager eyes and laughing lips,
   And problems of a thousand choices,
With loaded trees, and lucky dips,
   And Christmas-time in all the voices!
You scarce can push your way along
   Behind the window—which discloses
*Outside* the little ragged throng
   With longing eyes and flattened noses.

## HOLLY AND MISTLETOE

Fetch in the holly from the tree
   We fetched it from of old—
If plentiful the berries be,
   The winter will be cold;
The winter will be cold, my lads,
   For Providence takes care,
When creatures want and food is scant,
   That birds shall eat their share.

Undo the ancient mistletoe
   From oak-tree's hollow form—
If it be thick with balls of snow,
   The maiden will be warm;
The maiden will be warm, my lads,
   For Providence takes care,
When mirth and light reign half the night,
   That boys shall kiss their share.

## THE WEEK AFTER

Thou that diest, Thou that never diest,
Thy day of birth has come and gone again,
Heaven has sung Hosanna in the Highest!
And Earth has sung Peace and Goodwill to Men!

And some have feasted, and still more have fasted,
But in the week that now has slipped behind
The movement was a warm one while it lasted,
And hearts of men were willing to be kind.

Oh, keep that movement warm, not only now
But in all weeks that still beyond us lie!
Oh, keep that movement constant in us, Thou
That ever diest, and wilt never die.

## THE CAROL SINGERS

They come in ones and twos and threes,
   Small ragged girls and boys,
Whose homes will show no Christmas-trees,
   Whose stockings hold no toys;
And shuffling on the step at night,
They—sing? Well, to be kind, not quite—
   They make a sort of noise.

Not in the hope of myrrh and gold
   And frankincense they sing,
As they a hackneyed verse unfold
   About a new-born King.
They rate their gabbled effort at
A penny, and it's scarce worth that
   When they go carolling.

A try-on? Yes. But as for me
  I never can refuse
The rough unpractised minstrelsy
  That tells of heavenly news.
A child once in a stable lay—
How can I empty send away
  These children from the Mews?


## THE MUMMERS

Here's greeting for the master,
And for the mistress greeting,
And greeting for each gallant lad
And every pretty sweeting,
And greeting for the little children
Dancing round our meeting.

We be your servants all,
We be merry mummers;
We know jolly winter's face
Though we ne'er saw summer's;
We come in wi' the end o' the year,
For we be Christmas-comers.

This here do be Saint George,
This the heathen Paynim,
Dragon he will drink your healths
When Saint George has slain him;
This do be a beautiful maid
And a trouble 'twere to train him!

There's our mumming ended
And nothing to distress ye—
Surely, we be little loth

Since so kindly press ye.
Here's God bless ye, master, mistress,
All the house, God bless ye!


## A STOCKING TO FILL

Here's Christmas come round,
And a stocking to fill!
Oh Baby, sleep sound—
Lie still, Joan, lie still.

But wait! What is wrong
With your stocking, my Joan?
It is surely too long—
How your stocking has grown!

Can this limp thing, I beg,
Hanging lank in my view,
To-day fit the leg
Of the baby I knew?

Do you think—do you think
If I put back the clock
Your stocking would shrink
Once again to a sock?

Ah well! what's the use?
To think stockings won't stretch
Is the thought of a goose!
Come! the presents I'll fetch.

For here's Christmas, and so
There's a stocking to fill,
Though the baby must go,
For she cannot stay still.

## STOCKING-TIME

The Christmas hour I love the best
   Is in the dark of early day,
When Someone comes to break my rest
   Bearing a stocking stuffed and gay.

And crouched upon my bed, she cries,
   "Perhaps *you've* got a stocking, too!"
And I shall find with great surprise
   I *have*—and wonder how she knew.

Then she will laugh, and I will smile
   And round her tuck the eiderdown,
And we will watch each other while
   The treasures which our stocking crown

Are rifled from their bulging legs
   With many a happy ah! and oh!
Till both disgorge their golden dregs,
   The orange in the stocking-toe.

And everything she greets with glee
   Will fill me with amazement keen,
And all the treats prepared for me
   She will pretend she's never seen.

Old Daddy Christmas once, to fill
   My stocking, would down chimneys climb;
Now Little Daddy Christmas still
   Takes care I'm not past Stocking-time.

## FOR THEM

Before you bid, for Christmas' sake,
Your guests to sit at meat,
Oh please to save a little cake
For them that have no treat.

Before you go down party-dressed
In silver gown or gold,
Oh please to send a little vest
To them that still go cold.

Before you give your girl and boy
Gay gifts to be undone,
Oh please to spare a little toy
To them that will have none.

Before you gather round the tree
To dance the day about,
Oh please to give a little glee
To them that go without.


## THE CHRISTMAS-TREE

I set a little Christmas-tree
In my workroom just for me,
Hung with many a gleaming thing—
With lines of tinsel shimmering,
And ruby balls and gold were seen,

A trumpet, and two blue-and-green
Glass peacocks, silver nuts as well,
A Father Christmas, and a bell.

Then Twelfth Night came. And I took down
The ivy-trails, the holly-crown,
The bunch of pearly mistletoe—
The time was come for all to go.
But looking at my Christmas-tree
I thought, "It seems a shame to me
To put the pretty thing away
When it will yet last many a day."

And so I took the little pot
Between my hands, and when I got
Outside I went to Perrin's Court
Where little children play and sport.
Tinkling and twinkling on my way
I went, and they all stopped their play
To gaze at my bright Christmas-tree,
And "Oo!" they cried, "Oo! Ooo!" at me.

So I know how a rocket feels
When in the midst of wondering squeals
Upon its glittering way it goes
And stars upon the heavens sows.
But rockets vanish in the air,
While still my little tree somewhere
Bestows its shining joys on two
Small children who are saying "Oo!"

## CRADLE-SONG FOR CHRISTMAS

Child, when on this night you lie
Softly, undisturbedly,
On as white a bed of down
As any child's in London Town,
By a fire that all the night
Keeps your chamber warm and light:
Dream, if dreams are yet your law,
Your bed of down a bed of straw
Only warmed and lighted by
One star in the open sky.
Sweet you'll sleep then, for we know
Once a Child slept sweetly so.


## THE CHILDREN'S CAROL

Here we come again, again, and here we come again!
Christmas is a single pearl swinging on a chain,
Christmas is a single flower in a barren wood,
Christmas is a single sail on the salty flood,
Christmas is a single star in the empty sky,
Christmas is a single song sung for charity.
Here we come again, again, to sing to you again,
Give a single penny that we may not sing in vain.

## NOW EVERY CHILD

Now every Child that dwells on earth,
  Stand up, stand up and sing!
The passing night has given birth
  Unto the Children's King.
    Sing sweet as the flute,
    Sing clear as the horn,
    Sing joy of the Children
    Come Christmas the morn!
    Little Christ Jesus
    Our Brother is born.

Now every Star that dwells in sky,
  Look down with shining eyes!
The night has dropped in passing by
  A Star from Paradise.
    Sing sweet as the flute,
    Sing clear as the horn,
    Sing joy of the Stars
    Come Christmas the morn!
    Little Christ Jesus
    Our Brother is born.

Now every Beast that crops in field,
  Breathe sweetly and adore!
The night has brought the richest yield
  That ever harvest bore.
    Sing sweet as the flute,
    Sing clear as the horn,
    Sing joy of the Creatures
    Come Christmas the morn!
    Little Christ Jesus
    Our Brother is born.

Now every Bird that flies in air,
　Sing, raven, lark and dove!
The night has brooded on her lair
　And fledged the Bird of Love.
　　Sing sweet as the flute,
　　Sing clear as the horn,
　　Sing joy of the Birds
　　Come Christmas the morn!
　　Little Christ Jesus
　　Our Brother is born.

Now all the Angels of the Lord,
　Rise up on Christmas Even!
The passing night will bear the Word
　That is the Voice of Heaven.
　　Sing sweet as the flute,
　　Sing clear as the horn,
　　Sing joy to the Angels
　　Come Christmas the morn!
　　Little Christ Jesus
　　Our Brother is born.


## FOR ALL


Thy cradle was a manger,
Thy lodging was a stall,
When Thou wast born into the world
Once and for all.

Thy steed it was a donkey,
Thy shelter Mary's shawl,
When thou-began'st thy journeying
Once and for all.

Thy infancy was cloudless,
No tear didst thou let fall,
Till time was come to weep for **men**
Once and for all.

## THE SHEPHERD AND THE KING

The Shepherd and the King,
The Angel and the Ass,
They heard Sweet Mary sing
When her joy was come to pass;
They heard Sweet Mary sing
To the Baby on her knee.
Sing again, Sweet Mary,
And we will sing with thee!
*Earth, bear a berry!*
*Heaven, bear a light!*
*Man, make you merry*
*On Christmas Night.*

The Oxen in the stall,
The Sheep upon the hill,
They are waking all
To hear Sweet Mary still.
The Baby is a Child,
And the Child is running **free.**
Sing again, Sweet Mary,
And we will sing with **thee!**
*Earth, bear a berry!*
*Heaven, bear a light!*
*Man, make you merry*
*On Christmas Night.*

The People in the land,
So many million strong,
All silently do stand
To hear Sweet Mary's song.
The Child He is a man,
And the Man hangs on a tree.
Sing again, Sweet Mary,
And we will sing with thee!
 *Earth, bear a berry!*
 *Heaven, bear a light!*
 *Man, make you merry*
 *On Christmas Night.*

The Stars that are so old,
The Grass that is so young,
They listen in the cold
To hear Sweet Mary's tongue.
The Man's the Son of God,
And in heaven walketh He.
Sing again, Sweet Mary,
And we will sing with thee!
 *Earth, bear a berry!*
 *Heaven, bear a light!*
 *Man, make you merry*
 *On Christmas Night.*

## A CAROL FOR CHRISTMAS EVE

We come to your doorstep
To sing you a song,
Our tune is but simple,
Our voices aren't strong.

We sing of a Baby
As old as he's new—
Now welcome the Baby,
And welcome us too.

The Babe had no cradle
To rock him to rest.
The arms of the Mother
Rock all babies best.

The Babe had no garment
Of silk and of gold.
Her own mantle kept him
Within a blue fold.

The Babe had no mansion
In which he might roam.
He lay on her bosom,
And that was his home.

Each year as the times comes,
We too come along
To stand on your doorstep
And sing you a song.

We sing of a Baby
This night born anew,
For the sake of the Baby
God bless me and you.


## MARY'S BURDEN

My Baby, my Burden,
To-morrow the morn
I shall go lighter
And you will be born.

I shall go lighter,
But heavier too,
For seeing the burden,
That falls upon you.

The burden of love,
The burden of pain,
I'll see you bear both
Among men once again.

To-morrow you'll bear it
Your burden alone,
To-night you've no burden
That is not my own.

My Baby, my Burden,
To-morrow the morn
I shall go lighter
And you will be born.


## THE ENDING OF THE YEAR

When trees did show no leaves,
    And grass no daisies had,
And fields had lost their sheaves,
    And streams in ice were clad,
And day of light was shorn,
    And wind had got a spear,
Jesus Christ was born
    In the ending of the year.

Like green leaves when they grow,
    He shall for comfort be;
Like life in streams shall flow,
    For running water He;
He shall raise hope like corn

For barren fields to bear,
And therefore He was born
  In the ending of the year.

Like daisies to the grass,
  His innocence He'll bring;
In keenest winds that pass
  His flowering love shall spring;
The rising of the morn
  At midnight shall appear,
Whenever Christ is born
  In the ending of the year.

## SWEET ASS

Sweet Ass, go gently, go,
  By night and day sang she;
Rock gentle as a cradle
  Or a mother's knee,
For thou must bear my Baby
  As thou must bear me;
O do not break his slumbers,
  Go gently, go, sang she.

Sweet Ass, go steady, go,
  She sang by night and day,
Go steady as the coffin
  Is borne upon its way,
For thou must bear my Baby
  The road he cannot stay,
O do not break his slumbers,
  She sang by night and day.

'Twixt earth, she sang, and heav'n,
  Go gently, go, sweet Ass,
  Much lower than the stars are,
  Just higher than the grass,
This journey keep my Baby
  From either as we pass,
And do not break his slumbers,
Sweet Ass, she sang, sweet Ass.


## A MANGER SONG

Whence got ye your soft, soft eyes of the mother, O soft-eyed
  cow?
We saw the Mother of mothers bring forth, and that was
  how.
We sheltered her that was shelterless for a little while,
We watched the milking Babe at her breast, and we saw her
  smile.
Even as we she lay upon straw, and even as we
Took her sleep in the dark of the manger unfretfully,
And when the dawn of the strange new Star discovered her
  thus,
The ray that was destined for her and for Him fell also on
  us;
The light passed into her eyes and ours, and full in its flood
We were first to behold the first mothering look of the
  Mother of God.

## CHILD'S CAROL

When there dawns a certain Star
Comes a Stranger into the city;
The feet of prayer his dear feet are,
His hands they are the hands of pity.

Every houseplace rich and poor
Shall show for welcome a sprig of green,
And every heart shall open its door
To let the Stranger enter in.

I will set my door ajar
That he may enter if he please;
The eyes of love his dear eyes are,
His brow it is the brow of peace.

Through the heart of every child
And man and woman in the city
He shall pass, and they be filled
With love and peace and prayer and pity.

## SHALL I TO THE BYRE GO DOWN?

Shall I to the byre go down
　　Where the stalled oxen are?
Or shall I climb the mountain's crown
　　To see the rising star?
Or shall I walk the golden floor
　　Where the King's feast is spread?
Or shall I seek the poor man's door
　　And ask to break his bread?

It matters not. Go where you will,
　　Kneel down in cattle stall,
Climb up the cold and starlit hill,
　　Enter in hut or hall,
To the warm fireside give you cheek,
　　Or turn it to the snow,
It matters not; the One you seek
　　You'll find where'er you go.

His sandal-sole is on the earth,
　　His head is in the sky,
His voice is in the baby's mirth
　　And in the old man's sigh,
His shadow falls across the sea,
　　His breath is in the wind,
His tears with all who grieve left He,
　　His heart with all who sinned.

Whether you share the poor man's mite
　　Or taste the king's own fare,
He whom you go to seek to-night
　　Will meet you everywhere;
For He is where the cattle wend,
　　And where the planets shine—
Lo, He is in your eyes! Oh friend,
　　Stand still, and look in mine.

## WAKE UP!

*(Freely adapted from the Old French)*

Neighbour, what was the sound, I pray,
That did awake me as I lay
And to their doorways brought the people?
Every one heard it like a chime
Pealing for joy within a steeple:
     "Get up, good folk!
Get up, good folk, 'tis waking-time!"

Nay then, young Martin, know you not
That it is this our native spot
Sweet Love has chosen for his dwelling?
In every quarter rumours hum,
Rumours of news beyond all telling:
     "Wake up, good folk!
Wake up, good folk, for Christ is come."

Neighbour, and is it really true,
True that the babe so small and new
Is lying even now among us?
What can we lay upon his knees
Of whose arrival angels sung us,
     What can we give,
What can we give the child to please?

Dickon shall bring a ball of silk,
Peter his son a pot of milk,
Colin a sparrow and a linnet,
Robin a cheese, and Ralph the half
Of a big cake with cherries in it,
     And jolly Jack,
And jolly Jack a little calf.

I think this child will come to be
Some sort of workman such as we,
So he shall have my tools and chattels,
My well-set saw, my plane, my drill,
My hammer that so merry rattles,
     And planks of wood
And planks of wood to work at will.

When we have made our offerings,
Saying to him the little things
Whereof all babies born are witting,
Then we will take our leave and go,
Bidding good night in manner fitting—
     So, so, wee lamb,
So, so, wee lamb, dream sweetly so.

And in a stable though he lies
We in our hearts will soon devise
Such mansions as can never shame him.
There we will house and hold him dear,
And through the world to all proclaim him:
     "Wake up, good folk!
Wake up, good folk, for Christ is here."

## TAKE HEART, SWEET MARY

*(Freely adapted from the Old French)*

*Joseph.*    Take heart, the journey's ended,
        I see the twinkling lights
    Where we shall be befriended
        On this the night of nights.

*Mary.*    Now praise the Lord that led us
    So safe unto the town,

Where men will feed and bed us,
   And I can lay me down.

*Joseph.*   And how then shall we praise him?
    Alas, my heart is sore
That we no gifts can raise him
    Who are so very poor.

*Mary.*   We have as much as any
    That on the earth do live,
Although we have no penny
    We have ourselves to give.

*Joseph.*   Look yonder, wife, look yonder!
    An hostelry I see
Where travellers that wander
    Will very welcome be.

*Mary.*   The house is tall and stately,
    The door stands open thus,
Yet, husband, I fear greatly
    That Inn is not for us.

*Joseph.*   God save you, gentle master!
    Your littlest room indeed
With plainest walls of plaster
    To-night will serve our need.

*Host.*   For lordings and for ladies
    I've lodging and to spare,
For you and yonder maid is
    No closet anywhere.

*Joseph.*   Take heart, take heart, sweet Mary,
    Another Inn I spy,
Whose Host will not be chary
    To let us easy lie.

*Mary.*   Oh aid me, I am ailing,
    My strength is nearly gone,
I feel my limbs are failing,
    And yet we must go on.

*Joseph.*   God save you, Hostess, kindly!
    I pray you, house my wife
Who bears beside me blindly
    The burden of her life.

*Hostess.*   My guests are rich men's daughters
    And sons, I'd have you know!
Seek out the poorer quarters
    Where ragged people go.

*Joseph.*   Good sir, my wife's labour,
    Some corner let us keep.
*Host.*   Not I! Knock up my neighbour,
    And as for me, I'll sleep.

*Mary.*   In all the lighted city
    Where rich men welcome win,
Will not one house for pity
    Take two poor strangers in?

*Joseph.*   Good woman, I implore you
    Afford my wife a bed.
*Hostess.*   Nay, nay, I've nothing for you
    Except the cattle-shed.

*Mary.*   Then gladly in the manger
    Our bodies we will house,
Since men to-night are stranger
    Than asses are and cows.

*Joseph.*  Take heart, take heart, sweet Mary,
    The cattle are our friends.
  Lie down, lie down, sweet Mary,
    For here the journey ends.

*Mary.*  Now praise the Lord that found me
    This shelter in the town,
  Where I with friends around me
    May lay my burden down.

## FAREWELL TO THE OLD YEAR

We saw thee come in, a wee naked babe,
  A wee naked babe in the cold:
We see thee go out, a tottering wight.
  A tottering wight and old.
But we will remember thee in thy youth,
  When thy boyhood was green and bold,
And we will remember thee in thy prime,
  When thy manhood was clad in gold.
Though we see thee go out, a tottering wight,
  A tottering wight and old,
All to make way for a wee naked babe,
  A wee naked babe in the cold.

## WELCOME TO THE NEW YEAR

Hey, my lad, ho, my lad!
  Here's a New Broom.
Heaven's your housetop
  And Earth is your room.

Tuck up your shirtsleeves,
  There's plenty to do—
Look at the muddle
  That's waiting for you!

Dust in the corners
  And dirt on the floor,
Cobwebs still clinging
  To window and door.

Hey, my lad! ho, my lad!
  Nimble and keen—
Here's your New Broom, my lad!
  See you sweep clean.

**THE END**

# Index

# Index

A Carol for Christmas Eve, 217
A Christmas Lullaby, 204
A Dragon-Fly, 145
A Drink of Water, 95
A Kitten, 88
A Manger Song, 221
A Stocking to Fill, 209
A Wish, 165
After Rain, 144
After Tea, 92
Air-Balloons, 108
Alphabet, 49
Ambush, 146
Annar-Mariar's Christmas Shopping, 204
Autumn Crocus, 148
Autumn Rain, 147

Baby Stands, 192
Bedtime, 92
Bell-Song, 19
Bethlem Bells, 75
Between the Bars, 126
Blind Alley, 110
Bliss, 47
Blow the Stars Home, 169
Boasting, 38
Books, 51
Boredom, 90
Boys' Names, 124
Bravery, 24
Breakfast, 86
Broken Wing, 172
Burning the Gate, 152

Carol of the Signs, 72
Cat!, 38
Catch It!, 122
Child and Dog, 87
Child's Carol, 222
Chilly Dawn, 147
Choosing, 122

Circus, 158
City Streets and Country Roads, 166
City-Under-Water, 180
Class-Room, 49
Close of Day, 123
Comforting, 120
Cradle-Song for Christmas, 213
Creeping Jenny, 182

Dancing, 59
David, 29
Dog, 37
Doves and Starlings, 167
Down! Down!, 188

Earth and Sky, 200
Echo! Echo!, 189
Economy, 189
Elizabeth Cried, 123
Em, 27
English, 54
Epitaph, 48
Evening Hushes, 166

Fairies, 191
Farewell to the Old Year, 228
Farms, 8
Fat Hans Schneider, 23
Fie, Fie!, 188
First Gathering, 67
Food Out-of-Doors, 110
For a Cloud, 171
For a Cock, 169
For a Dance, 13
For a Dewdrop, 174
For All, 215
For Christmas Day, 71
For Good Morning, 194
For Good-Night, 194
For Mary and Her Kitten, 9
For Them, 211

# 234 *Index*

Fred, 33
French, 56
Friend or Foe?, 40

Geography, 52
Getting Out of Bed, 84
Girls A-Weeping, 189
Girls in the Garden, 139
Girls' Names, 125
Going Into Dream, 97
Going to Bed, 93
Good Morning, 85
Gossamer, 149
Grand-Dads, 190
Griselda, 31
Groundsel, 188

Heel, 41
Heigh-ho, April!, 138
Hey! My Pony!, 24
Hidden, 113
History, 51
Holly and Mistletoe, 206
House Coming Down, 105
House Hunters, 137

In Bed, 96
In Goes Robin, 114
In the Week When Christmas
   Comes, 199
India-rubber, 54
Inside, 40
Invitation to a Mouse, 191

Jabbering in School, 60
Jenny, 36
Jenny White and Johnny Black,
   112
Jill Came from the Fair, 116
Jim at the Corner, 102
Joan's Door, 159
Jolly March Wind, 66
Joseph Fell A-Dreaming, 132

Keep Still, 113
Kennel, 43
Kingfisher, 167
Knowledge, 50

Latin, 55
Lead, 42
Leaves, 138

Lessons, 87
Light the Lamps Up, Lamplighter!,
   10
Lilliput, 141
London Sparrow, 109
Long-Green-Hill, 132

Marmalade, 192
Mary Indoors, 90
Mary's Burden, 218
Mary's One, 3
May Meadows, 68
Meeting Mary, 3
Midsummer Eve, 69
Minnie, 34
Missy Sinkins, 144
Moon, 44
Moon-Come-Out, 133
Moonlight, 143
Morning Glory, 186
Morning Light, 142
Mrs. Peck-Pigeon, 108
Music, 58

Nan, 28
Nearly, 173
Ned, 35
News! News!, 64
Nine Red Horsemen, 18
Nothing, 47
Now Every Child, 214
Numbers, 53

Oh, Hark!, 168
Ol' Red Thief, 25
Old Wife's Song, 127
On the Staircase, 93
Organ-Grinder, 8
Ornithology, 57
Our Mother's Tunes, 187
Outside, 41
Over the Garden Wall, 83

Pantomime, 157
Pencil and Paint, 171
Penny Royal, 185
Peter, 35
Poetry, 58

Questions, 61

Ragged Robin, 183

Rainbow, 172
Rats!, 46
Rhyme, 192
Riding in Belmary, 124
Roasting, 38
Robin to Jenny, 202
Rules, 62

Sand, 5
School-bell, 48
Seven-sisters Roses, 168
Shall I to the Byre Go Down?, 223
Sing for Your Supper, 17
Sisters, 111
Six Green Singers, 201
Snow, 4
Snowfall, 98
Snow in the Garden, 158
Soldiers and Horses, 100
Some One to Tea, 91
Spoilt Child, 120
Spring in Hampstead, 157
Stocking-time, 210
Strawberries, 14
Sue Went to the Fair, 117
Summer Fountains, 141
Sun and Wind, 169
Sweet Ass, 220
Sweet Herbs, 140

Take Heart, Sweet Mary, 225
Teacher, 59
The Archer, 189
The Bell in the Leaves, 146
The Bells in the Valley, 188
The Birds Know, 14
The Bonfire, 152
The Bonny Bride of Kent, 128
The Boy, 104
The Bride, 193
The Brown Birds, 203
The Buttercup Field, 112
The Carol Singers, 207
The Child and the Bird, 78
The Children's Carol, 213
The Christmas-tree, 211
The City Show, 103
The Crack of Light, 160
The Daisies, 193
The Elm-tree, 150
The Ending of the Year, 219
The First Blackbird, 136

The Flower-seller, 9
The Garden in the Dark, 140
The Gate in the Wall, 133
The Golden Cat, 88
The Hills Over the Water, 195
The Kerry Loon, 181
The Light Heart, 22
The Lights at Night, 97
The Lost Farthing, 163
The Mark, 145
The Mellow Time, 150
The Milk-cart Pony, 101
The Mother Sings, 119
The Mother's Song, 77
The Mother's Tale, 76
The Mummers, 208
The Night Will Never Stay, 11
The Old Man's Toes, 161
The Pear Tree, 139
The Peddler, 26
The Quarrel, 89
The Riding of the Kings, 74
The Second Birth of Roses, 149
The Shepherd and the King, 216
The Smoke, 109
The Song of the Fir, 130
The Sounds in the Evening, 94
The Sounds in the Morning, 83
The Start, 135
The Street Fountain, 106
The Sweetstuff Wife, 164
The Tale of Lilla, 175
The Talking of the Trees, 129
The Tired Tree, 151
The True Tale of Grandfather Penny, 107
The Two Sweethearts, 131
The Village Green, 115
The Waves of the Sea, 12
The Week After, 207
The Willow-wren, 18
The Wind, 13
The Wind Has Taken the Damson Tree, 70
The Witch! The Witch!, 190
The Wonderful Clock, 181
There Isn't Time!, 86
This Holy Night, 73
This Year—Next Year, 65
Through a Shop Window, 206
Tippetty Witchet, 125
To Any Garden, 134

To Michaelmas Daisies, 148
Tom, 32
Treasure, 170
Two Penn'orth of Chestnuts, 191

Universe, 64

Vegetables, 7
Verbs, 56
Vet, 43

Wake Up!, 224
Waking at Night, 96
Waves, 5
Welcome to the New Year, 229
What I've Been Doing, 99

What Should I See?, 21
When Jane Goes to Market, 11
When the Almond Blossoms, 20
White Horses, 128
Who'll Buy My Valley Lilies?, 20
Why?, 121
Wildflowers, 6
Wild Thyme, 184
Windfalls, 170
Window-boxes, 106
Wolf!, 45

Yawning, 62
Yellowhammer, 6

Zodiac, 62

N-36